Tightwad Energy

a novel
by
Michael Frederick

Books by author:

White Shoulders

Places

Ledges

Blue River

The Paper Man

Different

Missouri Madness

Zed

Shy Ann

Drop 50 & Magnify

Summer of '02

Autumn Letters

Stuck

Indie Writer

King of Slugs

Golly Springs

Already Bad/Volume 1

Already Bad/Volume 2

Odd is Left

July, 2018/1st printing/2000 copies
Copyright 2018
all rights reserved

Cover design by Paul Coy
www.paulcoy.com

Back Story

That's my dad's quote on the back cover. I found it typed on a page standing in his electric German typewriter the day after he was found dead in his Van Nuys studio apartment in L.A. My mom said *he pulled a William Holden* by falling down hard when dead-drunk, hitting his head on his claw bathtub. David Daniel Wadstone was just another talented man that drank himself to death because he never realized his dream. So, I'm the 21-year-old son of a failed screenwriter. My name is Billy Wadstone. My father's goal was to see one of his scripts played out on the big or little screen. Never happened. He got close several times. There were several anxious periods of hopeful waiting after he'd found a lead in the business he'd submitted one of his scripts to.

My mom and I were always his first readers. I can remember being 8 years old and thrilled while reading his teleplay episodes for *Gunsmoke, Rawhide, Perry Mason;* and my favorite series, *The Twilight Zone.* The three of us had so much fun watching *our shows* on TV every week. We knew the cast of characters as well as any ardent fan possibly could. Crystal, my mom, would make this big batch of popcorn with shredded cheese and chili powder. I'd sit between my parents holding

1

this big bowl of popcorn on our couch that my New Age mom covered with her colorful *master chakra blanket.* We'd dig into the bowl without taking our eyes off the TV screen, taking in every frame. My mom was good at real-sounding dialog; my dad had this dark sense of dramatic comedy he called *dramady*, a script genre term he often took credit for creating. He didn't.

My left-handed dad would be sitting there eating popcorn while watching the show when *this idea* would pop into his head, and with pen-in-hand he'd jot it down quick into his notebook placed on the left arm of the sofa. Later we'd discuss this idea. Like in this one Gunsmoke scene, he'd have gimpy Chester break his *good leg* after falling off his horse:

"Next scene," my dad had our attention, *"Doc's fixing Chester's leg in his office near the back window..."*

Then my mom would take over the dialog, imitating Chester's plaintive whining drawl, *"Doc, how am I ever gonna walk again?"*

Next, my dad's dark, dry wit would take over: *"Chester's eyes follow Doc's eyes to the window with the old grumpy Doc peeking over his spectacles, scratching his chin while both men see the outhouse in back; Doc says, I wouldn't worry about walkin'. I'd be more concerned about what you're gonna do when ya get there."*

My mom would *laugh*, and if her laugh was loud enough he'd type it up on that huge German typewriter he called *Herman.* Many times, my mom collaborated with my dad if he asked for her help. He'd often use her suggestions in his stories, especially her better-sounding

2

dialog. Seeing my parents happy together and working as a team was good for my emotional maturity when I was young; yet, it was difficult to watch over time how intimacy was diminished to separate bedrooms for them by the time I was in high school.

They lived together too long…for my sake… eventually separated then divorced, all while still living under the same roof in our Culver City house. It became normal to watch my parents ignore each other while living in the same house; this went on until I graduated from Culver City High in 1972. For the next 3 years until I hit 21 –I was a *Deadhead,* a lazy pothead. More about that later.

My mom was always into all things related to natural healing, including Eastern religions, attending seminars and classes, and even these weird Buddhist chanting sessions she'd take me to in the L.A. area when I was too young to resist. Crystal Wadstone was a natural at networking. She'd memorize every person's name she met at these gatherings, taking in new information all the time. Little did they know that when my mom was a little girl named Crystal Sapp and being raised in Council Bluffs, Iowa, by good foster parents with her *big sister* Verla, who was 3 years older, my mom had this *gift* of being able to read peoples' emotions behind any *mask.* In high school, Crystal told Verla she was fat because she was sad about *something.* That *something* was that Verla had been sexually molested by their biological father when she was 11. Once Verla knew this red-hot source of her sadness with the same sense of clear knowing that her sister had – Verla was then able to lose weight fast. Even when little Crystal could *feel* all these emotions in strangers, she

3

had this uncanny ability to release it. She had taught herself not to take on the energy from others. My mother started to get a reputation for being able to read chakras, giving *master chakra readings* that were helping these people work on their interior lives, to help them manage these 7 chakra organs of the body that manage energy. Crystal learned that chakras are the body's vortices. So, I wasn't surprised when my mother opened our house every Saturday to these happy *clients* of Crystal's Chakra Tea Club.

My dad helped my mom get her home business rolling fast by calling all of the business cards she was given over the years, offering them a free master chakra reading by Crystal, a name they all knew well by then. Meanwhile, my dad was in the throes of wholesale rejection letters from agents, TV producers, and other leads he'd found during his weekly 20-hour *tightwad energy* gig at home. He meant *that* as a positive way to conserve energy and still put himself *out there* by using the least amount of energy possible *"at the speed of sound in my underwear,"* he'd often validate to me before he'd start telling me about *a story* he was working on. His stories were the things that he loved to talk about; that was my dad's passion.

My mom and I were always aware of anytime D. D. Wadstone had a script returned with a rejection letter to add to his collection taped to his cluttered office/bedroom wall across from his desk. Crystal said all those rejections of his work were a *toxic/motivator* to never quit, to never give up on his dream. Those times when he was recently rejected…were periods of healing for all of us…until once again we'd *hear* the sound of Herman's keys pounding away behind his closed office

4

door, it's electric-thudding strike quick and deliberate. Mom and I agreed that it had *the sound of a new story that would sell.* That hopeful *sound* of Herman's keys striking hard on that white copy paper, pounding out words of narration and dialog with all those standard script settings that would move with the push of a button, stop…and continue striking page after page. We could tell when he was onto something good by the *sound* of Herman coming from the other side of his closed door. It was a beautiful *sound* of hope to all of us.

Over time, my dad started drinking more at home while he worked in his bedroom/office with private bath; our house location another reminder of his failure, just a few blocks from major movie studios, MGM and Culver. Crystal let *Dave* have their master bedroom because she knew he needed the larger bedroom for his hours of pacing he'd do while telemarketing or thinking about the story he was working on. We'd listen to him on the phone from behind his closed door, delivering his quick pitch about a restaurant nearby offering a 2-for-1 lunch special this month, *"Just mention Tightwad called."*

Tightwad was my dad's nickname in Omaha, where he was born and raised. My dad told me his friends gave him the nickname because of *Wadstone*; and because *"I'm a tightwad,"* he admitted, going on and on, explaining his theory regarding the withholding of money by the people who raised him.

Over the years I could tell that his voice was *less happy* when he made his calls. The more he drank, the harder it became for him to sustain the energy it takes to deliver thousands of friendly messages for his clients.

5

My mother, Crystal, said that she understands why he drinks; and, *"He'll quit when he breaks the ice and sells his first script."*

The only *ice* Dave Wadstone ever broke, was the ice for his bourbon and Cokes he'd have with his Kools, a powerful menthol cigarette that I had to smoke too, whenever I'd sneak one out of his pack and walk around the block in my Deadhead stupor.

Crystal-Clear Words of Life

"*There's plenty of time...for jealous boys.*"

Until recently, I couldn't remember why I wrote that quote in one of my early notebooks; I'd be acting like my dad and jot things and ideas down before they were *lost forever,* as my dad would say. Then I figured out that it had to be around the time when Crystal's Chakra Tea Club was filling every parking space on both sides of our street every Saturday from 10 to 3 P.M.

There would be 20 to 25 interesting women of all ages; they'd be seated on the tile floor of our large sun room that had plants and speakers in every corner providing oxygen and relaxing New Age music to these women dressed in such colorful clothing. I'd hang out and watch sometimes, because there always seemed to be a mother who brought a daughter my age. It was exciting...but I never showed that it was. My mom would practice on me and my dad her master chakra readings. From her readings I was a *Green* most of the time…ever since I was 7, about the time she explained to me what that meant:

"It means your dominant fourth chakra is green, close to your heart…and Greens are all about energy."

That's all she said. But then as I got older and interested in girls from afar, and after hearing her give several readings, I asked my mom what master chakra for a girl is best suited for me right now. I couldn't believe how fast she knew right away that *"Yellow is best in every way,"* she pointed to her belly at the location of the 3rd master chakra below the heart.

Every Saturday, one of my mom's *clients* would bring a treat for all to share with Crystal's *tea flavor of the week.* One time, I was about 15 and this beautiful girl about my age in a *yellow* sun dress was helping her mother carry in the treat for this particular Saturday. I made sure I could hear *her reading* later when my mom said this girl was an "Orange." I remember feeling disappointed at first, but then I realized how much I believed in my mother's readings, even more than her regular hundred-plus clients. I just remembered that *"jealous boys have plenty of time"* came from one of the *tea ladies* who made a joke about her jealous husband to the group. I asked my mom about it later (after jotting it down in my notebook) and she told me that *"time drags for jealous people,"* explaining that, *"jealousy is not love and shows a lack of self-esteem."*

***

My mom helped me sort through my dad's possessions about a week after he was cremated and after we scattered his ashes from a Culver City hilltop that he always liked to hike to alone not far from our house. The only thing I wanted of his was his old-varnished pine manuscript crate that held all his writing, including 37 copyrights of TV episodes and film screenplays registered with the Library of Congress. There were dozens of filled notebooks that I was determined to glean and put into a story that I could publish someday to honor his struggle to become a validated writer. In one of his notebooks, in his familiar handwriting, I read about one of his favorite topics:

"If I was a young man today, I'd find some easy product to sell to small-town businesses in the Midwest, back to my roots where tightwad energy thrives and time slows to a pace I can handle. To each customer I would let them know I'm a writer, that I'm putting my stories together in a book that I plan on selling to them when I publish it. My customers would become my readers who'd support my writing from then on. Plant, tend, then harvest. Tightwad energy is the withholding of appreciation for every little thing in my life that I'm responsible for creating. This is harder to do in a place like L.A. Anyone, anywhere, who lives in tightwad energy, knows there is never enough in your life...and that's exactly what you'll get...just enough to survive in the reality you've created. 90 per cent of us (including myself) stopped practicing gratitude. We withhold it, fearing we have to hold on to what we have...including gratitude. I saw it up close when I was a boy, when Omaha was a cow town by the river. I saw it living in the eyes of my family and friends and watched it spread into the eyes of any lover I ever had. I want to warn my son that he has to go to the mirror before he's old, to find the strength to see this normal/insanity, this mask

we've all created. That's the only way to destroy it: to accept it and begin loving yourself first...as if you've had no past. I want to tell my son to start over young and use all his youth to find an easy product in order to reach his dream. I failed to do this because like a million other lone wolves out there -I let harmful addictions run me."

***

I don't know why I bought into my dad's lost youth by taking what he'd said and written to heart, knowing instantly that I had to stop this life of a Deadhead when I turned 21. It came to me at the speed of sound, a phone call from a woman I'd never met. It was my only chance to give meaning to my father's life, even if posthumously. My mother knew and understood it, telling me that *"children or babies learn to mimic the vibration of the adults who surround them, long before they learn to mimic their words."* Besides that: my dad was a *Green* too. That's why I painted the outside of his crate green and the interior yellow. Yellow was my mom's idea, since she convinced me long ago that I had to pay attention to that color if I wanted to live the best life I could.

2 Days to Verla

I was 21, writing in this *notebook* on a Greyhound leaving L.A., headed for Woodbury, Iowa. It's 1975, the beginning of my roaring 20s and the beginning of this 1500-mile 2-day bus ride to live with my Aunt Verla in this small city named Woodbury in Northwest Iowa. It's amazing how I wrote for 2 days straight on that bus; I know I was weaning myself from Deadhead to zero, which was a habit for me ever since my dad gave me a hit off his pipe in the parking lot before going into Disneyland. I was 14. He wanted us to see Disneyland stoned. We did. And there's no better memory for me than that trip into Walt's world while stoned with my dad. More about that later…maybe.

My desire was to arrive at my destination fresh and alert after writing 50 pages in my tightwad energy "T.E." notebook, or 100 pages if you count front and back. It was a writing assignment from Verla, my mother's older sister I'd never met. During holidays I remember hearing her *booming voice* on the phone. This was about a year after my dad died when my mom informed me that she was selling our house and moving to Ensenada, Mexico, to start a new life with her girlfriend, Valerie, my high school Spanish teacher. I know my mom's relationship with "Val" is why my dad finally agreed to

11

a divorce after being separated for 5 years. No way was I going to move to Mexico, not caring *"how close Ensenada is to San Diego,"* my mom and Val reminded me. My mom didn't want me to get my own apartment in L.A.; so, Crystal called her big sister, this waitress/manager in Woodbury, Iowa, a woman I'd never talked to until my mom handed me the phone after I heard Aunt Verla's powerful voice on the phone, telling my mother in a *funny way*, *"Put his lazy ass on the phone. I want to talk to him..."*

With the self-esteem of a depressed pothead loser who barely graduated high school 3 years ago, I said, *"Hello,"* holding the receiver a safe distance from my ear when this voice of a confident woman stated clearly:

"Billy, this is your aunt, Verla. I know we've never met, but I've got room here for you to crash rent-free and a job bussing tables at a cafe I manage. You can save some money quick here, Billy...and get your own apartment asap."

I couldn't hear myself when I kept saying, *"Okay,"* in this self-imposed depressive stupor I hadn't been willing to shake since my dad died.

"Get all your clothes packed. And Billy, your mom tells me you're a writer like your dad. I have this job for you on your bus ride here..."

"What's that?" I thought I asked when this rising *sensation of hope* came over me.

"I want you to buy a big notebook with pencils and one of those tiny, twisty pencil sharpeners, you know?

"Yeah..."

"And I'll pay you fifty bucks for your life story that I'll read when you get here. I want to know everything a young writer knows about his life...from way back. All the good and bad stuff, Billy. All the good and bad shit your parents did. I won't judge you for it. We got a deal?"

I thought I said *"Yeah"*; but I was stoned and into my head about my dad's writing in his notebooks I'd been reading every night since he was cremated.

That was it. The next thing I knew, I was on one of those Greyhound window seats near the back of the bus riding along with my dad's writing crate that held my dad's work and Herman, now stored with my suitcase in the luggage compartment in the belly of the bus. For the first time in my life I was writing up a storm...*about me.* I'd never written about me before. And I'd only written assignments in school that were so boring...I damn-near came close to being short a couple credits and not graduating with my class. My biggest concern up to this drastic move was handled in December of '72 when my draft lottery number was 360, *too high* to get drafted. And I stayed that way...until recently.

I wrote early-on between L.A. and Vegas:

"To write about myself is new. My mother taught me at an early age by example, to be consumed with your life until you have something positive to share with others. My mom did it with her chakra tea club; my dad never did sell any of his writing. So, I've seen success and failure up close. And I don't plan to fail."

I remember rolling into the Vegas bus terminal for an hour lunch break; I kept writing until the driver told

13

me I had to get off. I wolfed down a hot dog and a bag of chips with a Coke in *the terminal café* and craved one of my dad's Kools, so I bought a pack and walked outside in the Vegas heat, getting dizzier by the puff. I quit weed for this venture and now had to at least smoke something…even it was bad at first…I knew it would get better after a few more Kools. It always did. I was thinking about *things* I'd written, words that Aunt Verla was shelling out fifty bucks for and would be reading soon. Things like:

"When I was just starting grade school my dad would send me out on little errands just to get me out of the house…even at night. He'd tell me to go outside and discover something new. My mother was the opposite: she'd tell me to stay in my room with a good book. Then, I'd hear them arguing about such things, which made me want to leave the house just to get away from their noise. My mother was a master chakra expert, well-known in this field of 'sprout heads,' (my dad used to call her clients) who came to our home in Culver City every Saturday for these esoteric chakra readings and 'adjustments,' she called them. I spent many Saturdays around such people, mostly women, who have this interesting way of looking at these 7 chakras that they all believed played a role in keeping mind, body, and emotions working in harmony. My mother called these chakras, 'soul-rays'; and I can recall seeing her clients as some of the happiest and well-balanced people with real light in their eyes. I'd rarely see this light in people anywhere else outside our home. By the time I was in high school I had a different way of looking at people. My mom wanted me to tell you that I'm a Green most of the time. Most of us Greens are healers who want

14

harmony in our youth and think we can move up to Blue
just by being into music or writing a book. I want to stay
in the Green and slip up to Blue now and then, but then
dropping down, between Green and Yellow...I feel more
real there. This is the kind of dialog my mom and I
would have every day. She tried to give me vocal
training regarding activating all 7 chakras by chanting
each chakra's sound up the scale at bedtime, until
eventually I found myself chanting to myself in school at
difficult moments until I was convinced there is
something to this vibration of energy I'm responsible
for. I noticed about me (in high school) that I was able
to pivot myself from a negative emotion to a positive one
by giving my mind positive images and no thoughts. I
had to do this pivoting more and more in high school my
junior and senior years, since I was a lone wolf, not into
sports after failing to make the varsity basketball team,
except I did enjoy going to games. I resented the
attention jocks got from girls, when writers like me and
my dad were pretty much ignored. That's why I'm on
this bus, passing this desert landscape while thirsting for
a way to validate my dad's life as a writer, a dedicated
writer who never sold any of his life's work. My dad
was like this consistent gold miner, a prospector who
looked for the mother lode in solitary ways from his desk
phone. That didn't work. I want to try something else,
something I don't know yet. All I do know is that if I
give my attention to this story about tightwad energy -I
will find and create the essence of it by staying
positive."

***

All through the night and Utah, under an overhead
reading light I wrote, seeing nothing but my moving

15

pencil on the page; except every now and then I'd look out at the blackness and see these isolated homes that reminded me how lucky I am, lucky to be headed to someone at the end of the line.

Nearing my 2nd day of this traveling-while-writing marathon, after shaving away two #2 pencils, and with the western side of the Rockies in view, I'd see a serviceman in uniform seated a few rows up and I'd jot a note down, something I'd left out of my notebook for Verla:

"A big break came my way when my draft lottery number was 360, a high number that would never be drafted. I know the draft lottery changed millions of lives for young men like me. I didn't have to become a man in the service. I could stay home and sleep away my life, smoke weed with my friends, hang out at the beach. I was lucky to get such a high number. My parents took me out to a Mexican restaurant right away to celebrate my 360. I felt lucky that night, because I was concerned about my future, and I didn't want to lose it in Viet Nam. So, I went back to sleep...for 3 years...until this bus ride to the heart of tightwad energy, the place where my father said he would go if he were a young man."

***

Even on a 4-hour Denver layover I wrote up a storm in the terminal, almost missing my bus if not for the friendly driver waiting a few minutes for me after his smoke break.

***

Before my next layover in Omaha - in the same area where my parents were born and raised - I wanted to write about young Verla, things my mother told me about her sister, yet I was torn about Verla reading it in my notebook. Then: the *image* of my father's writing piled in that crate with Herman (his typewriter) and now riding with me in the belly of this bus with my luggage…made me start writing.

Young Verla

*"M*y mom said that her big sister was fat and sassy until Verla ran away from the foster home they shared in Council Bluffs, Iowa, a blue-collar packinghouse town across the Missouri River from Omaha. Verla was 18 when she graduated in May of 1950 or '51 or '52, I forget. I wanted to know about my only aunt, since I'd never met her; and, she's bound to be one of my main characters in "Tightwad Energy," this anything-but-lineal story that already seems destined to be labeled anything but a novel.*

The main reason I agreed to this move to Woodbury was because my dad said I was conceived there, in a boardinghouse a few blocks from where Verla worked. Dave Wadstone met Crystal Sapp on a blind date when they were both 18, a matchmaking set up by Verla for my future parents to attend a big band dance in a downtown Woodbury ballroom/nightclub. My dad's friends called him 'Tight Wad.' One of his friends was Verla Sapp, who waitressed at Sammy's Café and set up her baby sister on a blind date with this Tight Wad guy from Omaha, who worked as a driver/delivery man for an Omaha wholesale paper company. Tight Wad always had breakfast at least once or sometimes twice a week when Sammy's opened at 6, and before his morning deliveries to local Woodbury packinghouses.

My mother would talk about that day she'd taken a bus from Council Bluffs to Woodbury in the spring of 1950-something right after she graduated from high school; it was the first time in 2 years they'd seen each other since Verla left home for good. Crystal moved into a boardinghouse room in downtown Woodbury (that Verla paid for). Verla had lost 80 pounds in the two years since Crystal last saw her. When baby sister off-boarded her bus she didn't recognize her 5'3", 130-pound bulldog-solid sister. Verla was wearing a red wig with a red blouse and white calf-high sailing pants with her 2-inch heels, a transformation skinny sister Crystal couldn't believe.

Verla thought Tight Wad (Dave) was a perfect match for Crystal, and of course the boisterous waitress told them both just that long before they met in Sammy's on their blind date before the dance. Verla's date was a skinny guy, older than Verla, a business associate. They were seated at a table in Sammy's when Dave walked into the café. As Verla predicted -it was love at first sight for both of them. My mom told me that I wouldn't even be here if not for Verla setting up this blind date. Crystal had her own room in a boardinghouse on the first floor; she said the sourpuss landlady didn't allow any men visitors after 9 P.M. I was amazed at that kind of Puritan attitude back then, and my mom stated, 'David called it these tightwad energy rules for separating people, which caused the opposite effect. Dave would talk about this kind of stuff between dances, claiming that Woodbury and Omaha led the nation in teen pregnancy. And you know what Verla said? She yelled across the table: You hear that, Crystal? People like to have sex here! We all cracked up.'

My dad talked about that night he met Crystal and how Verla was with this skinny character who had money. Dave (my future dad) said Verla winked at him and ordered him to give Crystal a ride home because she wouldn't be home until tomorrow. Tight Wad said he had to sneak into Crystal's first-floor window that fateful night I was conceived."

***

After leaving Omaha, I was about 100 miles south of Woodbury when the bus crossed over the Missouri River and headed north up I-29. Out my east-facing window I could see the passing Loess (pronounced Luss) Hills, a stretch of hills in Western Iowa that my mother claimed was formed by eons of wind-blown soil that was only found here and China. My mom and Verla lived on these hills in Council Bluffs. My dad loved those hills and wrote about them in his notebooks. When Verla ran away to Woodbury she was 18, so their foster parents didn't go after her. My mom said Verla had to get away from that sugar-rich diet their obese foster parents provided, even though my mother remained thin in that environment.

Half-way to Woodbury from Omaha I ended my writing assignment for Verla. I kept watching those hills, knowing that Verla told my mother when she ran away, she hitchhiked in *the hills* alone…until a traveling salesman picked her up and gave her a ride to Woodbury. *"A stranger,"* was all Verla said when my mom asked her about this man who had picked up Verla hitchhiking in those hills. That's what I want to find out,

20

who that stranger was and what happened in those early days when Verla ran away and never came back. I could be like my dad and make up some story that might even be more interesting than reality. However, I also lived that isolated life of fiction my father made for himself in busy L.A., and watched it boil his life's work down to a crate full of words on paper. I want to dive into this story I've begun and take it as far as it can go, into this land of tightwad energy, this place where my dad said he would return to realize his dream to be a published writer…if he was young again.

Just then: with not many miles to go, from my billfold I removed 2 items from the bill compartment (that held three hundred dollars cash); they were in my dad's crate, this folded piece of faded peach-colored paper, something old that *Tight Wad* (my dad) read and copied down, words I wanted to put on the last page of my notebook that Verla would read:

"Fear is totally unnecessary, because its source comes from false assumptions of the ego as it navigates a shadowy dream world of illusion based on its own idea of separation. Time to act in a new and creative way."

Then, I opened the 2nd item, a magazine photo of a beautiful actress I'd seen before on TV that was taped to the inside lid of my dad's writing crate. My mom knew it was Donna Reed, and that she was from Iowa. I figured my dad wrote an episode for Donna's TV show or had her in-mind to play one of his characters in one of his spec scripts piled in no semblance of order on top of Herman. Week after week I'd picked through his writing, and I never found anything related to Donna Reed. Maybe she was like a pin-up girl, a favorite actress he admired. But then I went to my library and found her hometown, Denison, Iowa, a small town located just a few miles east of the magical Loess Hills that my father said he would return to…if he was a young man.

I don't know how I bought into my dad's lost youth, taking his words to heart (as Greens do) and realizing instantly when I heard Verla's offer -it was my chance to validate my dad's life as a writer. One of his notes I found in his crate; it was a quote my mother gave him that I mentioned earlier: *"Children or babies learn to mimic the vibration of the adults who surround them, long before they learn to mimic their words."*

My First Reader

By the time my bus drove into downtown Woodbury, I could imagine things working here; and, first chance -I had to get a map of the area and see the small towns located in this heart of tightwad energy. I could really *see* myself making a living here, in this markedly slower pace so alien to me.

Rolling into the terminal I saw a woman waiting for the bus door to open. It had to be her: a stout woman in her 40s wearing a mint-green waitress uniform with white thick-soled nurses' shoes and pink bobby socks. My mom warned me that she wore wigs. This one was a blonde Cleopatra-style and length with bangs. Then, her unforgettable voice greeted my bus driver with "Hey, Jerry!" as the friendly driver unloaded the baggage. I thought it was cool how the driver knew my aunt.

While off-boarding slowly down the aisle with my notebook, I saw her watching for me to appear with this *real anticipation* that I wasn't used to seeing. I couldn't remember ever seeing anyone so happy to see me. I wrote later:

"She yelled, 'Billy! You look like your dad!' and laughed so loud I could hear it bouncing around me off the walls

and high ceiling of the small bus depot. Her hug was strong against her solid stout body of maybe 180 pounds if I were to guess. She looked into my gray cold-turkey eyes and I could see past the pink lip gloss and extended eyelashes -and there were my gray eyes looking right at me. My parents have blue and green eyes. I remember my mom saying that her sister has gray eyes like me. I pointed to my suitcase and my dad's crate. That's when Verla impressed me, when she said to my driver, 'Jerry, are you stoppin' in for your free breakfast tomorrow?' Then she said to Jerry's confused face, 'Yeah, it's free if you help my nephew schlep this crate into the trunk of my car!' There was no hesitation: she picked up my suitcase and Jerry and I each carried an end of the crate outside and into the trunk of Birdie, Verla's rusted-out yellow and white Fairlane."

***

Sammy's dayshift manager parked Birdie downtown a few blocks from the depot in the alley near Sammy's delivery door that led into the café's clean kitchen. I followed her into the clean white-tiled dining area with its aqua-colored soda fountain counter stools and several matching aqua chrome tables and booths lining three walls that made this a good-sized café. It looked like one of those diners in Hollywood from the 50s without the headshots on the walls, and one other big difference when I looked out the front windows of Sammy's: very little traffic, pedestrians or vehicles. There was time to really look at things here. Then, I looked at my wrist watch and it was still on L.A. time. I set my watch by the wall clock near the kitchen, knowing I'd better get used to this time zone.

We sat in *Verla's booth* below a ceiling fan where she smoked a Winston while starting to read my notebook right after she'd served me my best meal in weeks, meatloaf with mashed potatoes and gravy with carrots and a fountain Coke. I devoured my first meal in my new home like a wolf, then I interrupted her reading to bum a smoke from her pack, since I threw away my pack of Kools. I could see her taking in the words I'd written. I didn't want to be here when she read about herself. Besides, I needed a good long walk, and she had over 2 hours of reading left. I used the clean bathroom in Sammy's after my smoke, feeling dizzy after telling her I was going for a long walk to stretch my legs.

"Good, good," my first reader said without looking up from my notebook, adding, "This is good. And I'm going to finish it in one sitting."

I stepped outside Sammy's front door, impressed by the attention my aunt was giving my writing, since I was used to hearing lip service from busy people who had no time for such things. I learned that big-time from D. D. Wadstone, my dad. It felt good to walk fast and stretch my leg muscles; and whatever that long stretch of writing was -it ignited something good in me. I had written over twenty thousand words, about things I'd never put into words before this trip. And every moment since arriving in this upper Midwest city of 80,000 -I could *feel* that I had returned home in some way. Not in the way that Thomas Wolfe returned to Asheville; but rather, a return to the place where my parents met and created me. Or, am I feeling what my mother truly believed: *"that we are Spiritual Beings having a human experience."*

25

I couldn't help from thinking about how my father lived here when he was my age as I walked block after block on the clean downtown sidewalk of this old river city that had this *smell* coming from the east, from one of the world's largest stockyards and packinghouse districts…not even a mile from here. The buildings and streets were old from weather; and there was only one building over 10 stories high as I walked into this drugstore to get another notebook and a map of the tri-state area I knew I would need.

I walked east in the direction of an older warehouse district like I saw in Omaha's Old Market District. It was a smaller version of Omaha with old brick streets and warehouses with moving freight train *noise* not far away as I enjoyed the slower pace of this city of industry and labor while high from the thought of *my first reader;* and I was anxious about her reading the part about my mother and Val, a nice lady my mom's age who taught Spanish in my high school. I thought I wrote everything I wanted to about their relationship…and wasn't sure Verla knew anything about her sister's relationship with Val. And that bothered me. I thought of other *things* she'd read by now as I walked along lower 4th Street, an area of seedy bars, including stripper bars, dive hotels with old warehouses and wholesale businesses.

I walked to and into a corner adult bookstore, Nort's Book Palace, after I saw through the dark glass of the front door a pinball machine near one of those old pop coolers. I bought a 16-ounce bottle of ice-cold RC Cola that lasted for 6 pinball games, including 2 free games I won from matching at the end of the game.

I returned my empty bottle of pop to the scowling old hag at the lone register; I'd seen plenty like her in Culver City and West L.A. small businesses. These were the *tightwads* my dad would skip calling in his directory, these mom and pop ethnic-run businesses that my dad said *played stupid/no speak English* on the phone. My dad didn't care for Jewish prospects because he'd been rejected by them for so long. I know he was jealous of their business savvy and labeled them all *tightwads,* stingy with a buck. My mother loved everybody and would tell my dad it was *not attractive at all* to hear him say negative things about anyone he didn't know. She'd remind him often that *we're all the same,* and; he'd just grab a beer from the fridge and go to his office where he could smoke a Kool while standing in front of his open window.

I left Nort's and knew by the time on my Timex that she'd be reading my chapter about my life in Culver City where *Oz* was made. Verla would be reading about how my mother's business was thriving more and more after my dad died, and a time when she was so happy she'd found Val. And I knew I had to write more about my dad's work I'd discovered in his writing crate the first chance I got, things I didn't want anyone to read.

Munchkins and Deadheads

"**F**or over a year after my dad died I could barely get out of bed before noon. I'd been reading a thousand things I found inside his crate, a million words that I sorted into piles of things I might put in my book. I was one depressed pothead and Deadhead. My mother believes that we choose our parents in order to advance to a higher consciousness eluded in past lives. In order to understand Billy Wadstone, it's important to know my 'chosen' parents. My mother, Crystal, was a good mother. If I had a problem, my open-hearted mother would say, 'A problem shared is a problem half-gone.'*

As my mom said earlier: my dad pulled a 'William Holden' by drinking himself into an early grave after hitting his head on his bathtub while drunk out of his gourd. Crystal had a key to his apartment and had a 'feeling' that I shouldn't go with her that day. She told me that his death made her want to put the house on the market and begin her new life with Val in Mexico.

*Ever since I can remember, my mother would read
my chakras; this was way back and before she even
knew she had this gift of reading these invisible lights
inside the body that Hindus have seen for thousands of
years. Her 'master chakra' was Green then, and she
said I was a Green 4th chakra too. She said that's why
we could have these heart-to-heart talks about anything
without issues or past drama attached. Crystal really
helped diminish my fears about moving to Woodbury
when she said, 'Billy, a young man with a Green master
chakra, who fears his future, has a good chance at living
well...because your parents are out of the picture. All
you have to do is abstain from alcohol and other drugs
and stay in your heart. If you are willing to give that
kind of attention for thirty days...your Green will light
up bright with aliveness again and give you the balance
any Green must have to reach their potential.'*

*My mom was right. I had to quit weed in order to
make my own way in a world run by tightwad energy.
My dad failed to let go of his addiction, and that's not
where I'm headed. So, the next morning I forced my
lazy butt out of bed, gathered all my stash, pipes, rolling
papers and bong, tossing them into a garbage bag with
all my Grateful Dead posters and tapes; then out the
door I went, headed for that magical place my dad
showed me when I was seven, right after we'd all
watched The Wizard of Oz in color.*

*As I walked down the clean sidewalk of our street
with all my Deadhead stuff slung over my shoulder -I
recalled vividly that time when my dad walked me these
four blocks to that wedge-shaped Culver Hotel, a 6-story
flatiron-shaped building that my dad said John Wayne
and Red Skelton once owned. We entered the hotel at*

29

*the wider end of the building's triangle and into the
main lobby, climbing this winding marble staircase that
my dad said, 'leads to The Land of Oz.' Climbing each
floor, D. D. Wadstone, the screenwriter, was narrating
while stopping on each floor's carpeted hallway, where
he showed me all these black and white framed pictures
of the Oz characters we'd just watched on TV.*

*Each ascending floor hallway of the hotel in this
heart of movieland had a new display of old Hollywood
movie stills. Between each floor in the narrowed
stairway my dad would talk about 'the ghost of the 6th
floor' where the Munchkins stayed while filming Oz.*

*Recently, as I climbed the same staircase to the 6th
floor with my Deadhead bag draped over my shoulder, I
could recall my dad's voice bouncing off the stairwell
walls, telling me in his Rod Serling voice that we were
going to one of the rooms where the Munchkin cast
stayed during filming. Tightwad producers made them
sleep 4 or 5 in a bed to reduce production costs. I
wanted to write about when my dad opened that door,
how I felt like I was seeing his world better than I ever
had when we stepped onto the rich forest-green carpet
with more pictures on the walls as he headed for a
corner room where a maid's cart was parked by the
open door to room 605. I thought it was cool how my
dad knew Spanish and talked to the maid in her native
language, enough so that she invited us into the room
with her. My dad pointed to the queen-size bed and said
to me, 'Imagine four, five Munchkins sleeping here
crossways like this,' he pointed; but then he pointed to a
small fridge and asked the maid in Spanish and in
English (for my benefit) if she'd heard about the ghost
who liked pistachio ice cream. The woman got excited*

right away, knowing this ghost story she'd heard from other maids here. My dad started to pace around this room like I'd seen him do a thousand times at home, this intense storyteller who paced around the bed pointing at it, and I'll never forget his words: 'Tightwad energy, Billy. This is a perfect example.' Then came his Rod Serling voice, the voice of The Twilight Zone's creator when he stopped pacing and pointing, looking right at me, Rod said, 'Imagine four, maybe five Munchkins sleeping crossways like sardines on a queen-size bed on the sixth floor of The Culver Hotel, only blocks away from a movie studio where Oz and Munchkins were made real to millions of viewers across the country. These Munchkins went to bed one night in this very room, and when they got up the next morning they found the fridge door was open and a container of pistachio ice cream had turned to liquid ice cream. Except something was missing: every pistachio was gone.'

I found myself standing in front of that same Munchkin room on the 6th floor that my dad showed me. I'm holding my bag of Deadhead stuff. Being in this hotel made me realize I was going back to another Oz, to another ghost from the past for my father; I was returning back to the land of tightwad energy, to a 200-mile stretch of hills 15 miles wide along Western Iowa and Missouri that were made almost entirely from wind-blown soil. He wrote that he would return to those hills today if he was a young man. Verla, I'll show you his writings I found about the Loess Hills. He said you and Crystal were raised there. He wrote that 'tightwad energy could be harnessed in those hills, and that it was the perfect location to make good things happen for a young man.'

31

Maybe it was because I was cold turkey and had more energy in my legs, but something seemed to make it easy to move down the carpeted 6th floor of that hallway while passing all those framed Oz characters on each side of me. My dad's long-forgotten words he'd said after leaving the hotel that day were now between my ears, so clear in his Rod Serling voice: 'The missing pistachios represent the rich, picking out the best of everything, leaving us Munchkins sleeping four in a bed and too terrified to do anything about it...'

I stopped at the end of the hallway and stared at the garbage chute and could see the memory of my father stopping on the sidewalk that day, and that inaudible febrile stammer of his when his ideas moved faster than he could speak them. He had to speak them aloud to me, to help him remember them until he could get to his office: 'Billy, the garbage chute on the sixth floor at the end of the hall represents the dark sucking hole that tightwad energy has squeezed into all of us little guys...' I can still see him alone with his thoughts as he picked up his walking pace home because he was anxious to get to his typewriter to pound out the episode he imagined delivering personally to Mr. Serling's secretary.

I opened the garbage chute and felt like I was stuffing my past life into that sucking hole, where soon I could hear that garbage bag falling into that same void of darkness that my father could never escape. Again...D. D. Wadstone never heard back from Mr. Serling or his secretary.

Verla, for the next 5 days and nights I struggled with anxiousness and lost sleep, stopping myself several times from going back to that hotel dumpster to recover my stash. Next thing I knew, I was riding on a bus, replacing my addiction with all these words that kept coming page after page and seemingly giving me more and more energy."

I'm Home

Knowing Verla should be close to finishing reading my notebook made me walk faster…until I was there, finding her still reading with quite a few Winston butts standing in her ashtray.

"I'm just about done," she said, flipping over the last page of my notebook, this woman who I didn't know whether to call Aunt Verla or Verla.

When she finished reading both sides of all 52 pages, she lit a smoke with her lighter and said, "You have to save this, Billy. It's good. I'm making copies of it, that's for sure. I don't want you to lose it."

"Really?" I thought I said.

"I loved the way you wrote about your life in Culver City… The movie studios, the Munchkin hotel… I didn't know that your dad was a set designer for Gunsmoke and Have Gun Will Travel? And he got fired for showing up drunk on the set," Verla laughed, which made me laugh, because her laugh was so real and funny-sounding. "And you were *so young* when some of this stuff went down. How did you know all this stuff?"

"My mom would tell me everything."

34

Verla nodded, knowing her sister was that way and told me, "Crystal could *never* keep a secret. I should've kept notes," she shoved her Winstons my way and I lit one. "You really kept me turning the pages, not wanting to stop."

That's when Verla reached into her uniform pocket, pulled out a wad of cash and counted out fifty bucks and handed it to me. I'll never forget that feeling for getting paid for my writing; and I was instantly aware that I'd already made fifty bucks more than my dad ever did from all his writing that was now safe in Birdie's deep trunk.

"Your mother told me you were into writing like your dad, and that you hate math. Did your parents encourage your writing?" she asked.

"No, not really. My mom encouraged me to read. I think it goes back to when my dad was fired for being drunk on the set. He took the TV out of the house. So, my mom would take me to the library. She said it was a blessing in disguise to not have a TV...that I could turn it all into a positive thing."

"She got that New Age stuff from our foster mother. Crystal always said I was a master Red chakra, and that my Orange gives me this *paroxysm,* she called it. I'll never forget that she told me my big laugh is all about the joyous energy I can't hold in. I've *always* had that," Verla laughed.

Then she started to search back into my notebook for something she'd dog-eared and read out loud: "When my parents stopped being a couple, I would see it in school too, this brutal kind of isolation. We are the

35

same, yet we're separated by an illusion of our separateness. That's when I started smoking, as a smokescreen from all the shit around me at home and in school."

Verla closed my notebook, handed it to me, and I saw that look I'd come to know pretty fast, when Verla had an idea. It was a far-away look that made it safe for me to see clearly her gray eyes, eyes that were thinking of something she could do for me.

"I'll make another deal with you," she said. "If you can write about your life every day for a month…I'll give you a dollar a day…thirty bucks a month. Write about the life you want to create for yourself…and make it happen, Billy."

I found myself getting pumped from Verla's positive energy; and I knew at this moment that I already loved this woman who gave my words attention.

"I'm doing work I love, Billy. I'm meeting and serving people here. I *love* my customers. Find a business where you can interact with your customers and *don't* look for jobs in the paper. Be your own boss when you're young and learn fast."

"I'll be bussing tables here, right?

Verla looked at me…until I looked away from her eyes, and I could just tell, by her openness, that she was wanting to say the right words I really needed to hear.

"Billy…working here…you *need* this. You have to start listening and talking to strangers in here. Have fun. Let it be your training for this tightwad energy thing you came here to experience. You with me?"

36

I nodded yes and kept listening to this wise woman who was actually responsible for me even being alive in this very same town where I was conceived.

"Billy, you have talent. And I'm not just sayin' that 'cause you're my nephew. I used to read some of your dad's stuff back when he was your age... I'll just say no comparison."

Then she talked about my job here bussing tables:

"Sammy said you can have twenty hours a week with weekends off. Well, I actually told him what hours you'll work, but he agreed. It pays four bucks an hour. He'll raise it to five bucks after a month when he sees you're a good worker and show up on time. I need to give our bookkeeper your social security card to make a copy."

I nodded back at her, knowing this eye contact was good for me...somehow. I reached for my billfold to get my social security card, keeping my attention on her.

"There's no benefits of course. You do know we *are* peons in an oligarchy?"

I had to say with my first real laugh since going cold turkey, "My dad said that *all the time.*"

"I always liked the way your dad saw the world. He was a different cat, wasn't he?"

Again, I nodded yes...and listened to this beautiful woman with her black lash extenders and aqua-blue eye shadow, who reminded me of my parents, sort of a mixed bag blend that I realized was all related to the fact that we were all from the same tribe of tightwads. And now I was sitting in a café located on the very hills my father wrote about, that 200-mile stretch and 15-mile-wide expanse of hills made from wind and soil over millions of years. *"Only one other place in China has hills like back home,"* I'd heard my parents say whenever they talked about living on and near these same hills right here under Sammy's.

"You can stay at my place until you can get your own crib."

Again, she paused to light another Winston with the flick of her lighter. I passed on another one. She was waiting for me to ask her something. I didn't.

"You start tomorrow at *breakfast rush* from six to eight. Then you do *lunch rush* from eleven to one. You get that three-hour break from eight to eleven, so you can get away and do things you want…like *writing your story*," she pointed to my notebook. "And call me Verla."

Finally, I said, "So if I write every day for a month I get thirty bucks?"

"Right, and I get to read it before I pay."

Then Verla gave me a tour of Sammy's while informing me that I get one free meal a day and all the pop I want. I was excited about my life for the first time and hoped it would stay with me, this energy that was new for me. I was anxious to write about my dad's writing crate on the first pages of my new notebook, a part of this story I didn't want Verla to read until I'd met her. Now, I could trust her with it. I remember reminding myself to tape

Donna Reed's picture inside the lid of my dad's crate, the way I found it…first chance I get.

***

Verla Sapp had made it all happen with ease. Before Verla: I only looked forward to weekends and summers because I could sleep more. I was this recent ex-Deadhead, now amazingly *alive* while riding in that old yellow and white Fairlane she talked to while driving me to her apartment:

"Don't you *dare* run outta gas, Birdie!" then she'd *laugh* so loud, like some kid who had run out of gas before, explaining that *Birdie's* gas gauge was broken.

"How do you know how much gas you have?" I asked when she parked on her parking space near the back entrance to the old 3-story Argo Hotel, a brownstone with 30 tenants and Tommy's Lounge.

"I get gas every 200 miles. I keep track," she showed me her little notebook on her dusty dash that had a pen attached to it.

She helped me carry my luggage and my dad's writing crate into the back entrance near the freight and passenger elevator. But first she wanted me to meet the owner of the building. I followed Verla into the lounge, where Tommy Argo was tending bar. He was Greek like his brother Sammy Argo, who was soon to be my employer at the café.

I found myself riding down to the basement in the freight elevator with Tommy while Verla watched my stuff on the first floor. My shrewd aunt had worked out a deal with her landlord, that I could take the dumpster out around midnight every Saturday night for the city to pick up Sunday mornings. Tommy agreed to take forty bucks a month off her rent while her nephew stayed with her...*until he gets his own place.*

After Tommy showed me how to block all 3 garbage chutes for all 3 floors and loaded the large dumpster onto the freight elevator, he rolled it back and opened the chutes again before showing me where I'd roll the dumpster every Saturday night on the hotel's back parking lot. Then, Sunday morning I would roll it back to the basement and open all the chutes again.

"Looks easy," I told the friendly old man who reminded me of that Rawhide TV series character, trail boss Eric Fleming.

Then Tommy gave me a key to the back double-doors that were locked after the lounge closed at 2 A.M. I appreciated this weekly duty I could do that Verla told me helped her save for her retirement. My mother said that Verla was a hard worker and a real tightwad who lived below her means, and that she probably saved most of her income. *"Verla always had money,"* my mom told me.

After we put the crate down beside my luggage, and before Verla unlocked her 3rd-floor apartment door marked *301*, she told me that everybody smokes on this floor, that this floor is for smokers only. Then she said:

"Tommy says if we burn the joint down, the non-smokers on the first two floors have a better chance at getting out." And she pointed to *302* behind her, telling me if I smell smoke coming out of that open dormer, it's from Klem. "One time, Klem left his hot plate on with a cinnamon roll and he fell asleep. Just knock real loud on his door and he'll get up. He's eighty-five, a retired pharmacist from Winterset. I've had to wake him up when his smoke detector goes off. He gets these blackouts for hours at a time…and if he's in one of his blackouts…it's a recipe for disaster."

Verla showed me a spare key under Klem's doormat, telling me while pointing overhead to Klem's open dormer to feel free to use the key if I hear his smoke alarm going off, since the old man is hard of hearing. Then, she picked up her spare key to her apartment under her doormat and gave it to me. I wanted to ask her why she lived in such a firetrap, but she beat me to it when showing me her 300-square-foot sleeping room with kitchenette and private full bath. I'd never seen a Murphy bed until she pulled it down from out of the wall. Pink satin sheets covered the bed and a 5-foot-long body pillow shaped like a penis rolled off the end of the bed. She *laughed* and tossed it on the bed, saying her boyfriend, Ray, bought it for her at a novelty store in Omaha.

"I could live in a nicer place," she said, "but it's like that tightwad energy your father talked about… See, Billy, the rich, poor and middle-class live like tightwads around here. Everyone does just enough to get by while saving a few bucks along the way. This isn't California," she *laughed* then said how she sleeps naked with no covers in the summer with the window always open; and that I could sleep on the floor under the open window and still get a breeze from the oscillating floor fan in the corner. So, my sleeping space was about 4 feet wide and between her only window and the foot of her Murphy bed. I leaned out her large open window

41

with no screen and saw Birdie parked directly under her window in the hotel's parking area that looked like a used car lot for tightwads. I remember taking a deep breath and saying to myself, *"I'm home."*

Good Change

That first week of sleeping on the floor in Verla's cramped studio motivated me to save at least fifty bucks out of my 80-dollar weekly pay bussing tables at Sammy's. Every night I'd get up to go to the bathroom and see her naked body sprawled out on her pink sheets with that floor fan blowing dancing swirls of satin mixed in with the *snoring* sounds of a drunken sailor who warned me that she's *slept this way her entire life.* Mom never mentioned that. I asked my roommate if I could put my bedroll in her giant bathtub and sleep in there, but she said she might get up at night and have to use the bathroom and didn't want me in there. I laughed, and was aware that I had laughed more this week than in my whole life in L.A. Sad, but true.

This first week – on my own – was the beginning of my independent way of life that I owed to Verla Sapp. I was writing good stuff every day about my new experiences, as well as things I wanted to experience… and getting paid for it:

"*My first day bussing tables at Sammy's, I met fast-talking salesman Tony Patino, a middle-aged Italian from Chicago. Tony is a Camel-smokin' janitorial supply salesman who Verla calls 'T.P.' To me, Tony was a sign I was on the right track, since he has the same job selling the same line of products as my dad's leading character in his screenplay 'The Paper Man' that I found in his writing crate.*

From Verla's dark sleeping room to Sammy's flickering florescent lights at pre-dawn, I'd find myself catching parts of Tony's constant banter while he enjoyed his burnt toast dunked in coffee while quoting things from the Woodbury News at the fountain counter during Sammy's morning rush of regulars that packed the café. Only Verla's distinct voice and laughter could be heard above the din that Verla called 'the morning feed.' That first morning was a scene that forced me to release any remaining self-made depression I was holding onto.

I'd stand at the kitchen entrance watching for a table to be cleared, hustling out to it with my gray plastic tub and dish rag, attacking the mess and cleaning the table top and seat if needed. I've never been so busy in my life during each 2-hour shift. Verla said that Tony was a tightwad like Tony's boss, Max Hermann (another good sign), whose wholesale paper and janitorial supply warehouse and office were just a couple blocks from Nort's pinball machine in Woodbury's old warehouse district. I'd walk to Nort's on my break and have a couple smokes Verla gave me while sipping an RC and playing a few games of pinball. Then I'd go outside and find a private place to write, somewhere I could sit and get this story out of me and onto the pages of my 2nd notebook that I knew wouldn't last me a month at the rate I was writing.

I'd overhear Verla and Tony having these quick chats without ever stopping to look at each other. It wasn't hard to figure out that she was saying things for my benefit, to see if I was paying attention to this 3-ring circus going on all around me during the morning feed. It was Verla who convinced Tony to put 'T.P.' between 'Tony' and 'Patino' on his 'Max Hermann & Co.' business card. And she told him to use green lettering 'like money' with a white background. Tony sat there on his counter stool with that pinched look of pain 'from 'roids' Verla would say to anyone in shouting distance when T.P. waddled in, toting his cheap double-handled sales case on gout-sore feet made worse by cheap shoes bought from a Jewish wholesaler 'that gave me a deal,' he'd say while pinching the end of a burning Camel non-filter into his cupped hand that would shield smoke from others by soaking the smoke into his nicotine-stained right hand. Verla would empty and move T.P.'s ashtray around to mess with him, reminding the salesman in harsh terms: 'Look, T.P., you smoke too much. I'll help you quit,' Verla sounded serious, then it became obvious how Tony was setting Verla up for the regulars within shouting distance when T.P. said, 'Okay, I'm in. How are you gonna help me quit smokin'...since I was ten when I started smokin' these same frigin' Camels?'

Every regular watched Verla with gape-jawed stupefaction lean closer to Tony's flabby-cheeked face and say, 'Close your eyes.' And Tony did. 'Remember that hypnotist friend of mine in Omaha...the veterinarian?' 'Yeah,' Tony's eyes were still closed and he still had a lit Camel in his left hand. 'He says he can put ya under, and right before slicin' off that 'roid your sittin' on...for how long now?' 'Thirty years,' Tony admitted to Sammy's laughing regulars until Verla said the hypnotic trance 'would bring back his puckering pain every time he lit a cigarette.' T.P. and all of us laughed while getting back to the busy-ness at hand. My Aunt Verla was showing me that only I could create my life the way I wanted it.

As the days went by fast, I pretty much had the busboy gig down; and I found myself listening to Tony more and more when he stopped in at 6 every morning. He'd stay until 8, then after tipping Verla five bucks (every morning) he'd pick up his cheap butterscotch-colored cowhide sales case from the floor and drive off in that old faded-blue Chevy station wagon he always parked in front of Sammy's. Tony told me that he moved to Woodbury when he was my age. Then he got married, worked for a cigarette wholesaler in Woodbury for 20 years before working as a commission salesman for Max Hermann for 12 years. One of the things he told me, was that if I want to make some real dough...he had the perfect line for a young man starting out, adding, 'If you stay with it...you'll be rich in four years.'

I kept listening to Tony, because Verla told me T.P. doesn't give people this kind of information unless he likes them and sees real talent. 'Rich in four years' got my attention...and me without any college..."

***

Every chance I'd get, I'd scribble down something Tony said in my 30-dollar monthly notebook that I kept for Verla. Again, after a month, she read my work right away and paid me cash. It took her 3 days to read it. Then we walked down a couple blocks from The Argo to Warrior Bowl and she bought us lunch in Al's Place, a nice bar inside a 24-lane bowling alley where she tended bar when she was 18, *using a fake ID*, she told me during our lunch there. All the while, she talked about my month of writing; this time she took notes. We must've spent a couple hours talking about something that was giving me purpose and the self-motivation I've been craving my whole life. One part she dog-eared and read back to me:

"My father's crate barely fit into Verla's closet, a 3-step walk-in filled with clothes; there were wigs of all colors and shapes covered by clear plastic bags and mounted on Styrofoam heads hovering above dozens of pairs of high heels standing on shelves as if on display. My suitcase had to be left on the floor tight against a wall and closed. She said she didn't want my underwear hanging out when her boyfriend, Ray, came over."

She stopped reading and *laughed* after saying, "I love it!"

Then she'd read something to me that she really liked: "Between games of pinball I'd take a swig from my RC and I'd hear footsteps creaking overhead in the upstairs apartment above the 'bookstore'; I knew it had to be Nort if his wife lurked near the register, her permanent scowl on her sagging face until a furtive man, some customer, would enter under the *tinkling* bell. These men reminded me of boys I'd known in high school that had issues with women. Nort's wife had to be a trigger for these men who would be in and out after buying a new magazine without eye contact or a word spoken. Then, before I'd begin another game I'd hear Nort's footsteps coming down a staircase at the back of the store; he'd have a cheek full of black licorice I could see when he'd swipe his black tongue over his dry lower lip that pooched out as if he was mentally challenged in some way."

The last part of our discussion about my writing was about her favorite chapter that I'd wanted to write about on my bus ride to Woodbury:

The Crate

"**A**fter painting the crate green and the interior yellow - the colors my mother said would best represent my quest for a life well-lived - I really got into reading the stories inside that crate. When I first lifted open the lid I could see Donna Reed's picture from a Hollywood magazine that was taped carefully to the interior side of the crate's lid, and alongside her beautiful face was the only original quote my mother credited to D. D. Wadstone: 'Tightwad energy never trusts the flow of love or money in either direction.'

I tried to read and organize some of the 56 lbs. of stories inside a crate that weighed 30 lbs. empty. Scripts and notebooks typed and handwritten in pencil, a lifetime of unshared work. One time I asked my dad why he wrote in pencil, and he said, 'That's my carbon footprint,' he'd chuckle with a beer or after sneaking a joint he didn't think I could smell in his bathroom when the vent fan was also on high.

Night after night I'd sort through the crate, until I stumbled onto one of his spec scripts, 'The Paper Man'; it was like finding a piece of this tightwad energy puzzle he always talked about in the Loess Hills, near Denison,

Iowa, where Donna Reed was from. In this love story, a toilet paper salesman falls in love with a beautiful woman in those same hills running north and south through most of western Iowa, the very hills where my mother said she and my father would park and 'fool around' until they could get their own place.

The deeper I'd get into the crate –the more interesting it became. I'd find 'anonymous' quotes like: 'It is easier to behave your way into a new way of thinking than it is to think your way into a new way of behaving.' And his teleplays got stranger when I'd read an episode of Gunsmoke, Have Gun Will Travel, and Steve McQueen's series –all with a bizarre science fiction theme with space aliens that belonged in a Twilight Zone episode. There was one Bonanza episode where Hoss was visited by one of these aliens in a dream who told him there will be a great fire from a solar flare event. Of course, Hoss was able to save the lives of neighbors and livestock, as well as the beloved Ponderosa.

It was my dad's 'Paper Man' script that I enjoyed the most, since the lead character peddled his line in a way that my father must've envied. It was the story of his life…if he was young again. If I could do what his character did in the very same territory, in a thousand small towns splayed out for 200 miles in Iowa, Nebraska, South Dakota and Minnesota… I would have my customers become my readers of my book I've titled, 'Tightwad Energy.' It's as if my dad has given me this blueprint to follow…a gift of sorts…I hope.

Another D. D. Wadstone quote: 'I'm from the land of tightwad energy, where millions like me escaped

America's Heartland; that place where the richest soil on earth is now being gobbled up by massive corporations eliminating the family farm. I realized too late that my audience was always there...back home. I know for certain that if I had stayed, spent my youth writing stories for them –they would've supported me. I know this now.'"

Jewish Clutter

I t was right after my 2nd month of writing when I was on my 3-hour break from Sammy's; instead of pinball at Nort's, I walked 2 blocks further west into the warehouse district to Max Hermann's warehouse/office. I wanted to meet Tony's boss, *the old Jew,* Tony called him. Tony said Max could give me 10% over cost on my *dream product*: 33-gallon heavy-duty garbage bags, the only line I'd need to get thousands of customers in the land of tightwad energy. Besides that, my dad's typewriter, Herman, was a reminder to me that I was on the right track.

It was good that Tony had me write down the price I should get, and T.P. let his boss know that I'd be stopping in soon; that way I should get the price Tony knows I should get as a jobber buying from a wholesaler. I kept the price and the sample bag I wanted a quote on inside my notebook. Max Hermann was going to be one of my characters, and I was ready to pay attention. I was doing what my dad did by carrying *my crate* in my notebook; I made a copy of Donna Reed's picture and taped it to the inside cover, along with this quote my mom admired: *"The illusion is we are only physical."* Another gem in the crate from H. D. Thoreau: *"The question is not what you look at, but what you see. "* I'd find myself looking at them every time I opened my notebook to write. Like now: as I wanted to write about things that were fresh and saw a ledge on Mr. Hermann's dock that I could sit on and write before I meet my future supplier.

There was a man unloading a pallet of sweeping compound adroitly with a power jack not far from the open warehouse door that Max shared with a wholesale tire company. The smell of rubber and the noise from the salvage yard across the street had this real sense of work going on as I opened my first pack of Winstons I'd just bought in Nort's. That's what I wanted to write about:

"I bought a pack of Winstons in Nort's for the first time. I could see Nort's wife (I assumed) lose her scowl for just a moment when I added nicotine to my other addictions: sugar and pinball. I had to come back into the store and ask her for matches. 'We have no matches,' she scowled. 'We sell lighters,' she pointed her bony hand that was so white for early September. I was a tightwad too, and left without a lighter, knowing I had to watch my money, since I'd saved about 600 bucks already, closing in on my own apartment. I'm used to the floor at Verla's, but I have to be asleep before she is, or the snoring is unbearable. Soon, I get to meet her mystery boyfriend, Ray, a traveling salesman who comes to town once a month or so. I just got a light for my cigarette from a man unloading a truck on Max Hermann's dock. Tony set me up to get my cost per case for heavy-duty 33-gallon garbage bags. It's the perfect line to sell around here. Tony convinced me of that. And it's just like the character in 'The Paper Man' who buys his product from a Jewish wholesaler in Woodbury.

53

My dad used to deliver this kind of product for an Omaha wholesaler when he was my age."

I had another smoke after seeing - who had to be Max - come out of his office door and sign a delivery slip for the truck driver. I wasn't prepared for the *Jewish Clutter* Tony warned me about. T.P. said about his boss, *"Only a Jew could prosper in that clutter of samples, catalogs and old invoices stacked 3 feet high with narrow pathways circling the office and obscuring a cheap desk piled with chaos."*

Above the hum of a dust-caked window air conditioner, I shook hands with the silver-haired slouchy-shouldered Max Hermann, introducing myself and reminding the old man that *Tony Patino referred me.*

"Wadstone," the blue-eyed Jew looked over his mail-order reading glasses. "You from around here?"

"No, I moved here from Los Angeles. My aunt, Verla Sapp, is a good friend of Tony's…"

"Verla! Yes! She's a good customer of mine. Didn't Tony say you work at Sammy's?"

"Yes. I bus tables there and I want to sell these heavy-duty garbage bags," I showed Max my sample that Tony gave me, then opened my notebook to the page Tony helped me create just for this meeting.

***

I walked out of that clutter feeling good about my new *dream line* Tony said I had to have in order to break the ice with these people, people he knew from thousands of cold calls who *"were a bit different from town to town.*

You'll see what I mean after a few days in the field."
Verla was a hot topic for old Max; he loved Verla, calling her the *best waitress in town.* The prices for my garbage bags were right on the money and I said I would pay cash and carry at first. He said that Verla's nephew was *good as gold* to him, and that was *no issue* with this nice old man who had to be in his 80s.

I got back to work 20 minutes early to eat my big meal for the day. As Verla served me, she wanted to hear all about my meeting with *Tightwad Max.* And I told her that everything went well and that T.P. said I could buy his old station wagon for two hundred bucks.

"Soon, you can start lookin' for your own crib," Verla smiled. "I'll be a reference and help you cover your rent if you're short."

Things were moving along well.

Chance and Habit

Writing this story every day for 2 months has given me something more than *control* in my life. I believe it's possible for me to be writing full-time in 4 years, like Tony said. I already have the makings of a true story with enough real material to stay in non-fiction with Verla Sapp playing my lead character I'd never begin to imagine in a novel. She was giving me great ideas for my garbage bag delivery business, like printing business cards and invoices with Tightwad Energy as my business name; and it could also be on my vehicle lettering.

"It's the perfect name for your business and your book. And your customers will know that," Verla stated with confidence.

Just the other day Tony said he'd sell me his old station wagon for $200, because his wife wanted him to get rid of it. He said I could make payments. Verla wanted to have her mechanic look at the engine and test-drive it herself first. I'm probably the happiest busboy in America right now.

Verla grilled me every day about everything relative to my future business. Whether at work or in her apartment at night she'd ask me questions about my product, which always produced my sample bag for the prospect to test while she pretended to be a prospect in the many different moods I would encounter. She even bought me a little hand calculator to figure sales tax I'd collect on every sale in 4 different states; and she had her accountant help me apply for my sales tax permits in each state. Tony said I should carry the permits in my sales folder.

T.P. helped me with my *intro* when I first entered a business. Since now Tony sold only by appointments he'd made by phone from his office at home, his advice was clear: *"Just get out there and learn by experience."* Verla agreed, sounding like my mother when she said, *"You can create your life from where you are now."* About this time, Tony's *chance and habit* started to take hold of me. I wanted to publish my own book and sell it to all my customers…all of it a young man's attempt at validating his father's life as an unproduced screenwriter. *Chance and habit* is what Tony preached to me and some of the old regulars every morning at Sammy's fountain counter, that *"a persistent salesman with a good line knows his numbers and wants to improve them day after day…until he creates his own line and gives himself a chance to prosper from his own habit."*

Then: I might be clearing off a table, thinking about what Tony said earlier, knowing he wasn't just a *"washed-up corncob salesman,"* that Verla jokingly called him. I'd want to find a moment to scribble some notes in my little notebook I kept in my back pocket with an attached mechanical pencil that one of Verla's customers gave her and she gifted to me. My dad did the same thing, always ready to write something down he didn't want to forget. Verla even mentioned a few times that I reminded her of my dad when she'd see me scribbling something down. Things like Tony's quote and what I saw: *"Every salesman needs chance and habit. And the only way that happens..."* TP would pause to snort his Camel smoke from his crooked Italian nose. *"...is by loving your customers."*

***

This was around the time of one of Ray's monthly weekend flings with Verla; she told me discreetly when I was at work having my big meal, "Ray wants to stop by my place around midnight tonight. I leave the door unlocked and I pretend to be sleeping when he comes into my apartment. I wear a different wig. He likes it. We both believe that the best sex we'll ever have...is with a stranger."

I could hardly wait until I could write that down in my "T.E." notebook, including how she *laughed* at the shocked look on my face while she smoked her Winston at our corner table in Sammy's. I told her, "Don't worry, tonight's dumpster night. I'll grab a nap, get up at eleven, take out the dumpster and walk down here to write."

"Good," she smiled at my writing habit. "I told Ray you moved out. So, please put your bedding and clothes in the closet."

"That's why I want to start selling my line, so I can get my own place."

That's when she reminded me that she wanted to test-drive Tony's car before I bought it.

Unfinished Boy

That night of Verla and Ray's *midnight quickie*, I awoke at 11 P.M. after napping for an hour on Verla's floor. Verla had set her alarm for 11:30 P.M. I could hear my *snoring* naked aunt on her Murphy bed as I dressed quickly in the dark before splashing cold water on my face. I was rested and knew this was my perfect time to get some writing done in Sammy's when all the characters of the night came out. A nice breeze was blowing in from Verla's large open window as I put my bedding and stuff away and left her door unlocked as requested.

After my dumpster duty I began my late-night 7-block walk downtown with my notebook and pencils inside my maroon writing Hazel I bought last week. It would be the perfect carrying case for my sample garbage bag, business cards, invoice pad and my recent pages of my growing manuscript. I was thinking about Ray, and the things I know about him: Ray Vining was 50-something, never married; he has a daughter named Nell, and he lives in Omaha. Ray works as a sales rep for a company that sells gloves, aprons and knives to packinghouses all over the Midwest. Three of Ray's big accounts were in Woodbury and South Woodbury in Nebraska. Woodbury used to be one of Ray's 3 biggest customers, including Omaha and Chicago. I started writing with a cup of coffee at my corner table in Sammy's before midnight:

"Woodbury is on Ray's company route every 2 months; however, he sneaks up to see Verla every month in his rental car for a midnight quickie before his Omaha appointments. That's why I'm here now in Sammy's. Verla calls this her 'quickie night with her little tiger' that she claims is 'mutually monogamous.' As for Ray, I don't know. I overheard Verla telling Bev, her wig supplier, that Ray takes these 'boner pills' that keep him going for hours. Sounds like a sex addict to me. It seems to work for both of them. None of my business.

It's just before these monthly visits with Ray that I see her the happiest. It starts about a week before Ray comes to Woodbury. Verla would eat only a few crackers a day with coffee, trying to lose at least 10 pounds. And she does. But then, after a couple days she starts nibbling at snacks, and smoking more Winstons; it's that period regulars in Sammy's call: 'Ray Day.' Then she'll buy a new outfit that fits her like a shark-skin glove, some sexy dress that shows off her cannon-ball boobs and butt. A few days before Ray Day she'll go see Bev at her wig store and get a new look. This time she picked out a short Doris Day forward-curl platinum cut with straight bangs. While Bev was styling Verla's wig I overheard my aunt talking about Ray: 'He's my unfinished boy,' Verla said to Bev. 'Are you talkin' about Ray or your nephew?' Bev cackled as loud as her favorite client.

On my walk here, I kept thinking about how Tony said that in a couple weeks I could go with him on his

Max Hermann route to Denison, Iowa, Donna Reed's hometown. He's going to help me 'break the ice' and let me pitch a few prospects along the way while I ride along and test-drive his station wagon. He wants to get rid of it and retire, or at least 'that's what his wife is making him do,' Verla told me. I told Tony about Donna Reed's picture in my dad's writing crate, and that's when he said he calls on clients in Denison every month, a perfect little town for my Tightwad Energy garbage bag sales."

Strangers in the Night

A couple weeks later, I was close to going with T.P. on my sales training day to Denison, before making my move to retire as a busboy. I gave Verla my notice, so Sammy didn't think I was leaving him without time to replace me. Both Verla and Sammy were known to bus tables without complaining until they hired someone that fit into this Midwest café that had more life in it than all the movie studios in L.A.

D. D. Wadstone's tightwad energy, the withholding of your own energy - which Crystal and Verla both say takes more energy to sustain - is survival at best. Crystal always dismissed tightwad energy as *nothing special that will ever make any difference in the world.* I resisted the urge to follow my dad's path of least resistance (his t.e.) by stopping myself from going to the library to make copies from the Denison Yellow Pages. My dad's way would've been to call a bunch of businesses to let them know Billy from Tightwad Energy in Woodbury would be in town to stop in and show you my sample of heavy-duty garbage bags *below store prices.* I figured I'd get the names of those who wanted me to stop in and sales would be that much better. That's what my dad would've done, break the ice at the speed of sound without putting himself out there in the world, and staying clear of face-to-face sales calls.

But this was Tony Patino's area of expertise; he'd done it both ways and I had to write down what he said during a morning rush, scribbling like a doctor, *"Surprise and timing beat speed...with a small-ticket item like garbage bags or the book you want to eventually sell your customers. If you called every prospect in Denison, half of them wouldn't be there or able to see you when you got there. Leave a card and come back next time when it's all over town this guy from Tightwad Energy sells a quality product. Use the phone for repeat customers or during bad weather when the roads are bad. When you're young...use your legs and meet them face-to-face."*

***

A few days ago, Verla took me to Al's Place in Warrior Bowl, where we sat at the bar talking with her old boss, Al, who Verla tended bar for here when she first moved to Woodbury. Al never let Verla buy any drinks when she came in. I noticed that she had friends like that in about every place we ever went together. Even when I went with her to her chiropractor's office when she needed an adjustment: no charge for Verla. That's how Verla and my mom are alike: many people love them. Verla was trying her best to give me practice at meeting strangers for my *business move* every place we went. She'd introduce me as her nephew she brought along *to keep an eye on her.*

I broke away from Al and Verla at the bar to play that shuffleboard bowling game before sitting down at a table to do some writing. That's when I saw this Barney Fife-type skinny middle-aged man in a butterscotch-colored polyester suit and string tie with cowboy boots flirting with Verla at the bar. It didn't make sense to me that she appeared to really like this guy until it dawned on me: *It's Ray, her boyfriend,* who surprised *his girl* and drove up early since a client had cancelled their appointment tomorrow in Omaha. I wasn't 100% sure it was Ray until Sinatra started singing "Strangers in the Night" from Al's jukebox *—Ray and Verla's song.* Two longtime lovers who kept their sex life alive by pretending to be strangers. I watched Ray walk from the jukebox over to Verla, ask her to dance, and they slow-danced while singing the words along with Frank. Now I love my Aunt Verla, there's no doubt about that, but I had to conceal laughing at this odd-looking couple who sang while staring at each other and grinding away on Al's saw-dusted little dance floor in front of the juke box.

After their dance, Verla came over to me and slipped me five bucks, telling me to stay away from her apartment for a few hours. Until now, I never really thought Verla had a love in her life —until I saw real happiness in her eyes. Instantly she had transformed into this woman in love; and I was so happy about *whatever* she saw in Ray Vining. I know Verla likes skinny guys, but this Ray-guy looked like a pencil wearing cowboy boots when he left the bar with Verla right after she introduced Ray to me. I wasn't impressed with her *little tiger.*

***

I wrote for a few hours in the bowling alley, where I could get away from the smoke and noise in Al's. I had to get down on paper what I knew about this obvious *Orange* Ray that Crystal taught me to see right away.

***

A few thousand words later, coming from above Verla's apartment dormer, I could hear the *sound* of a vacuum. She was vacuuming in her purple silk bathrobe, wearing her Doris Day wig not long after Ray's surprise visit. Right away she had to tell me all about Ray. I enjoyed seeing and hearing her gushing about this guy she obviously really was crazy about, this stranger in the night who looked like this plain shabby little salesman with tobacco breath and carried the musty scent of the road on him. Regardless, I had to open Hazel and write down what I was hearing. This was *real* life stuff, not some imagined scenes in Gunsmoke or Bonanza. What I was writing wasn't a novel…it was *my life's* characters strung together from my mind's point of view. Yet, I kept having this *Blue* feeling that my mother taught me to pay attention to whenever I felt it, this craving to trust this bunch of real characters that I believed would lead me to becoming a published writer. My father failed to put himself out there to get his work read by the public. I didn't plan on failing, so I looked up the chemistry reading for 2 *Oranges* in Crystal's master chakra chart I kept in my dad's crate: *a real good match for a fun-filled life of no regrets.* That's what Crystal told me when I called her to confirm what her chart said.

I had to write fast while Crystal talked on the phone, scribbling down notes as fast as I'd ever seen my father

do. Then I had to re-write it and make sense of it later.
This is what I came up with:

*"Doris Day was vacuuming in her purple silk bathrobe
after her midnight quickie with Ray, this musty little
salesman she calls her 'little tiger.' There was a red
lightbulb glowing behind her pink bedside lampshade
with lavender-scented candles burning in several places.
She put on a pot of coffee and we smoked Winstons on
the ledge in front of her huge open window as she talked
and I scribbled notes about the first time Verla met Ray
Vining. I could tell she wanted this in my book, to get it
all out, and so I kept listening and writing, often unable
to keep up with Verla's story:*

*'In the spring of 1950 I was a month shy of eighteen
when I left my foster parents and Crystal. I told Crystal
I'd make enough money so she could go to college. Our
foster parents were okay, but poor as hell. They were
New Age cool enough, and Crystal was always attracted
to that. Not me. Our foster mother said that Crystal and
I were master Oranges; both of us had this gift of clear
knowing, reading people quick. We abused it at first.
We used it to make other people like us. Later, Crystal
used her talent for helping others in her tea club.'*

Verla paused to let me catch up, replacing the red
lightbulb in her lamp with her regular bulb. Then I
asked her how she got to Woodbury, and kept writing:

*'I hitchhiked with all my clothes jammed into two
suitcases and two hundred bucks to my name. This
couple in a new red convertible picked me up. Ray was
driving and who I thought was his girlfriend, Jane, was
really a business associate. I told them I was eighteen,
moving to Woodbury to look for a job. They were*

*headed there too, and Jane told me that they both lived
in Omaha and that they were both from Denison…'*

I had to stop Verla and ask her if she knew that the
actress Donna Reed was from Denison. She knew that.
And when I asked her if my dad ever mentioned Donna
Reed or Denison, a negative nod answered that…and she
continued on with the time she first met Ray Vining:

*'Ray said he was looking at some real estate in
Woodbury. I'll never forget when I asked him what kind
of work he does… Ray and Jane looked at each other
and laughed. Jane said they'd buy my first meal in
Woodbury at Sammy's, and Ray asked Sammy if he
needed a good waitress and I was hired right
there…while having breakfast with this couple. By the
time Ray and Jane left Sammy's I had a job and a place
to stay in The Argo, a hotel that Sammy's brother
owned. Everything was going so fast and smooth for
me…I fell in love with this town.'*

*"Since Verla was off work tomorrow, we talked until 3
A.M. It was clear to me that Verla and Ray had this
'secret' relationship. She said that Ray would come into
Sammy's for breakfast once a month or so…with or
without Jane. He usually brought in a one-night stand,
some girl he'd met the night before in Omaha, Verla
'thought at the time.' Verla said that Ray, then in his
early 30s, was always polite, 'a real gentleman who
tipped really good.' One day, Verla said she was
complaining about wanting to make more money and
Ray told Verla about his buddy, Al, who owned a bar in
Warrior Bowl near The Argo and that he needs a
bartender for busy weekends. When Verla reminded Ray
that she was 18, and 21 was the legal age for alcohol in*

68

Iowa…she liked the way cocky Ray said it was no problem to get a fake ID for thirty bucks. Ray told Verla that Al won't ask any questions.

Before long, Verla was making more money tending bar for 10 hours on the weekend than she made at Sammy's for 40 hours a week. Verla liked making money and now was saving for Crystal's move out of the foster home when her baby sister graduated from high school in a couple years. That's how I came to understand Ray and Verla's relationship more, now that I know they are both flaming Oranges, born promoters and fun-seekers to the end."

Ice Breaker

Today is the day I hit the road selling with Tony and test-drive his car. I rode with Verla to work in Birdie, wearing new clothes she bought me for my new sales gig, Tightwad Energy. Every sales tool I needed was inside *Hazel*: a sample of my garbage bag, my stamped 'Tightwad Energy' invoice pad, business cards and pens. All orders cash on delivery. Tony already has 5 cases of my garbage bags in his station wagon that I paid Max for Saturday. I hoped to sell and deliver today all 5 cases. It's a very anxious day for me. I can't fail. I have to get that first sale that Tony calls my *ice breaker*.

While I had coffee at the counter, Verla was getting the café open for business, greeting cooks and employees arriving for the morning feed of regulars that seemed to pack Sammy's every morning for 2 frenetic hours. I was thinking of the other day when Verla let Sammy know I was going to sell garbage bags like Tony Patino. Sammy came over to me while I was clearing a table; he patted my back and wished me good luck, telling me to *come back and see us*. Right then it hit me that I didn't have the gift-of-gab like T.P.; or even the savvy business acumen as old Max Hermann.

T.P. walked into Sammy's toting his cheap two-handled cowhide sales case. He sat down next me at the counter, removed his morning paper from his bag, and before placing it on the floor…Verla had his coffee in front of him. T.P. wanted to see my business card. He liked it: *"Tightwad Energy/Billy Wadstone/save $ on garbage bags/free delivery,"* green lettering on white background.

"It's perfectly simple! I like it! T.P. snapped open his paper. "It's either buy now…or bye-bye."

Then Tony looked me in the eye and told me to leave a business card whether they buy or not, and say, "Maybe next time"; then he asked me how I came up with that clever name for my business.

Verla answered her friend when she plated-down T.P.'s usual breakfast of burnt toast dunked in fresh coffee: "Because everyone 'round here is a *tightwad*…and it takes a ton of *energy* to sustain it. And what's this two hundred-dollar car you want to foist-off on my nephew?"

"It's right out front," T.P. pointed with his Italian nose while dunking his toast into his black coffee.

"Give me the keys," she held out her hand.

***

In front of Sammy's I stood there with my hawk-eyed aunt and watched her take a look at all four tires on the old faded sky-blue Chevy station wagon before telling me, "Get in." The interior reeked of spent Camels in the full ashtray with samples and sales literature scattered about the cargo bed with cases of paper and janitorial

71

supplies that included my 5 cases of garbage bags. I wrote later in my notebook:

"The waitress in the mint-green uniform squinted at the odometer and said, 'It's got a hundred and twenty thousand miles on it,' while starting the engine, then flooring the gas pedal and looking in the rear-view mirror for signs of smoke from the exhaust. She tested the transmission and brakes at the first red light and told me, 'The thing about an old car like this...if it lasts you six months without much trouble...you can save money and get a better vehicle.'"

I loved her attitude. But then while driving she said:

"Offer T.P. one-fifty. Tell him it's got too many miles on it and it'll need tires soon."

This was the beginning of my positive, assertive sales attitude I was going to put out there, something my father failed to do. And I wondered if this could be the blueprint of tightwad energy he failed to follow, which led to his self-destruction. That other side of me was subtle, yet knew my mother was right all the time about us being Spiritual Beings having a human experience. I still didn't feel safe telling my aunt about something I found in my father's crate, a Twilight Zone episode he wrote. It was about humans afflicted by *time and suffering*, and how insanity is caused by believing we are all separated into our own tribes and not a united species. This was too way-out-there to even talk about now, yet I understood his meaning as I neared the time of approaching these different tribes who would see me as a stranger in their town on this first day of my new gig.

After I told Verla I didn't want to haggle Tony down on his price - since he was willing to let me make payments - I admitted I was living on tightwad energy and appreciated Tony's generous gesture. She agreed and laughed, "We're all tightwads here!"

I wanted my aunt's unabashed laugh and confidence; I have none of those traits that will help my sales today. Then I realized I was coming to that place in the road where I would soon find myself face-to-face with strangers; I was compelled to keep reminding myself of Crystal's words: *that every person was a Spiritual Being having a human experience.* My father could turn away from what he wrote about in his stories, because of his dualistic mind my mother spent many years trying to heal. And just then: Verla pulled into a full-service gas station owned by one of her *regulars* to have him install a pair of new windshield wipers. I was feeling the closeness of my *ice breaker* in this land of tightwad energy, this approaching much-needed first sale that D. D. Wadstone said he failed to get.

Tightwad Energy

"That 40-minute September drive on scenic 141 through the Loess Hills on the way to Denison was like any anxious first day of school or the first day on any job. T.P. rode on the front passenger seat of my cluttered 'first car' that Verla had Tony sign the title over to me after she paid him 200 bucks cash when we returned from the test-drive. Within minutes, and before Verla would let me go with T.P. – she called her insurance agent (another regular) from Sammy's office and arranged full liability coverage for me. Leaving Sammy's, Tony handed me the keys to the station wagon and told me he was glad to get rid of it, except, 'Now I use my wife's car,' he griped. 'She says it'll cut down on my smoking since I can't smoke in her car.' My first passenger lit a Camel and I reluctantly took one he offered as I drove away from Sammy's, leaving behind low wages for good...I hoped."

***

We cruised into Smithland, where T.P.'s only sales call was the town's biggest employer, a dogfood plant. I parked; he walked away coughing and hacking up phlegm so bad he had to stop and spit out a mouthful on his way to his big account. He pointed to a café on 141:

"Meet me there! She'll buy garbage bags. Good coffee, too."

***

I had my ice breaker in that café, selling 2 cases. T.P. was impressed when he came into the café and I was getting paid after delivering my first sale. I bought coffee-to-go, as I was anxious to sell my remaining 3 cases of product in Denison.

***

In Denison, I dropped Tony off at this huge packinghouse that Verla said was one of Ray's big accounts. It had to employ thousands by the sheer size of the plant and the number of vehicles in the massive parking lot. T.P. said he'd get a ride and to meet him later in *Bob's Bar on the square.*

***

Later that afternoon, nursing a Coke in a cozy booth in Bob's Bar I wrote:

"I sold my remaining product to 3 of the first 5 businesses in Denison I walked into. Then I kept going door-to-door introducing myself with my card, showing my sample and taking orders for delivery tomorrow. 8 more sales for tomorrow. This is the place my father said he would go to realize his dreams...if he was young again. I've never felt so alive. It seemed like every person I showed my card to was a buyer..."

I looked up from my notebook, and there was T.P., hunched over and nursing a beer on one of Bob's barstools; I could see that familiar worn *cowhide* sales

75

case on the floor beside him. He wasn't surprised by my good news, calling Denison a good town to work if you have a good product; *"It's a good place to start,"* he'd told me when leaving Woodbury this morning.

T.P. gave me a Camel; we toasted to my first day of freedom. That's when I saw Ray Vining's ferret-faced profile in the bar mirror; he was slouched over his mixed drink in a booth with a slender middle-aged woman. Tony wanted to introduce me to Jane, the woman with Ray. Then I remembered hearing Verla talking about some *Jane who lived in Denison, and that Jane and Ray have a daughter who lives in the area.*

But then, after Tony slugged back his draft beer, lit a Camel, he had changed his mind about going over to Ray and Jane's table. "I'll tell you in the car," T.P. said, and I followed him out of the bar without Ray or Jane seeing us leave.

***

On that drive from Denison with Tony, I was right about Ray being this guy who wasn't right for Verla.

"He's a horny son-of-a-bitch, and always will be," T.P. barked from the front passenger seat.

"You mean with Jane?" I was concerned for Verla.

"No, no, they have a daughter together. Verla, Jane and Ray go way back. This isn't the best time for Verla to know Ray was talking to Jane."

"Why?" I had to ask.

"Jane knows Ray fools around with certain girls…and

Verla wants to believe he's being this loyal boyfriend…"

"And she's loyal to him," I said.

"I know! That's what pisses me off! He's screwin' around and she's none the wiser!"

"How do you know?" I was curious.

"I know Ray. That's all I'm going to say. I just don't think it's a good idea to bust up Verla's fun. I mean, she *is nuts* about that skinny prick. So just promise me you won't tell Verla we saw Ray with Jane."

"Okay," I promised, knowing I *had* to write this down in my growing story.

I thought there was *something* about Ray that didn't seem right to me when I saw him with Verla; he did seem *phony* and not at all the kind of guy Verla would be so loyal to.

***

After Tony cleaned out his crap from my car, dumping it into his wife's trunk, he shook my hand and said, "She'll find out about her *little tiger* on her own."

I drove over to The Argo, parked in my new parking space directly under Verla's 3rd-floor window and realized I couldn't write about Ray or Jane, since Verla was still reading my writing every month. I told her she didn't have to pay me anymore, but she insisted. So, I'll have to write certain things in a separate notebook and hide them from Verla in my dad's crate.

***

That first full month of Tightwad Energy sales was by far my most thrilling month of my entire life. Four weeks of total freedom, walking into hundreds of small businesses, selling strangers a product they all use, and saving them all money. All of this was so easy for me in this land of ever-expanding tightwad energy. I was only following D. D. Wadstone's simple blueprint on how he'd publish his work. I'd found so many passages related to this in notebooks stacked inside his crate. He talked about selling *his line*, and how he'd tell every customer he was a writer and working on a book or a collection of short stories that he planned to publish himself, and that he hoped each and every customer would buy a copy. This was when I decided to title my book, "Tightwad Energy," and dedicate it to my dad.

Ray Day

By early November I was averaging 120 new *T.E.* customers a week, about 500 a month. I'm doing what my dad failed to do in this land of tightwad energy that he believed would support his writing…if he was young again.

I managed to convince Verla that I didn't want her reading my book; "*I want to surprise you,*" I told her. I wanted to write "T.E." as a memoir, a story based on the only *real lives* I knew. But Ray was changing all that; and, I had this *feeling* I'd be writing about things that might hurt Verla. It was important to me to stay far away from the imagined fiction that filled my dad's writing crate, nearly 60 pounds of sweat and disappointment that I'm certain had to have contributed to his alcoholism and early death. I had written around this time:

"I know I inherited Crystal's clear-knowing…about things like Ray Vining; a thousand times I'd seen my mother meeting a stranger invited to her tea club in our home. Within seconds of having her guest sit with her in front of an electro-magnet light my father installed in my mother's 'session room' adjoining our large sun room – Crystal would know the master chakra location without failing once. Ray is an Orange, like Verla, except he's

wired to go down to Red with all kinds of 'primitive behavior' my mom told me when I recently called her for advice.

I'm close to getting my own crib soon, saving money for my publishing venture and a van to hold more product, so I can stay out on the road for the whole week in my ever-expanding land of tightwad energy. I was thrilled to have been averaging 25 new customers a day, telling each one about the book I was writing and my goal to sell them a signed copy.

Every morning in Sammy's I'd begin my day with this positive energy coming from Tony and Verla. Tony would greet me as 'Mr. Tightwad Energy! How many customers do you have now?' 'Over eight hundred!' Verla would yell from the kitchen. 'This kid has a gold mine!' T.P. would point to my aunt, who always seemed to love Tony in a brotherly kind of way. This particular morning, Tony picked up on some familiar patterns he'd seen his favorite waitress display when 'Ray Day' was near. He'd compliment her new wig style, 'The Jackie O. with bangs' she picked out yesterday in Beverly's Wig Salon.

'It's Ray Day,' Tony chirped from behind his coffee cup.

'Tomorrow night,' Verla reminded T.P., displaying her smitten school girl act that had Tony and me laughing so hard when she growled in anticipation of her 'little tiger.' I was happy for her, until Tony discreetly whispered:

'Ray is a silent business partner who I don't care for personally. I don't like him leading Verla on about his loyalty to her...'

Verla came back to the fountain area and T.P. asked her if Ray was driving up from Omaha. 'Fort Dodge,' she said. That's when I saw T.P. take out his pocket notebook and scribble down something he handed to me discreetly. 'Fort Dodge Industries,' I said discreetly in the morning rush of Sammy's. 'Who's Bob Pilgrim?' I asked T.P. 'Ray's big customer. Biggest employer in Fort Dodge. Go see Pilgrim today. Tell him Ray referred you to him; and pitch him garbage bags...and find out where Ray hangs out. I'll bet you a hundred bucks he's got some Fort Dodge Verla in some strip bar.' Tony handed me his Max Hermann business card and told me to give it to Pilgrim. He knows me. He might give you an order...and something good for your book.'"

Fort Dodge Verla

I drove straight to Fort Dodge Industries, another massive packinghouse that Ray would call-on *once a month,* T.P. said, adding discreetly when I got up to leave Sammy's, "If you run into Ray, tell him I referred you to *Pilgrim.* Use Pilgrim's nickname: *Dane.*"

Seated in the waiting area of the purchasing department I had a chance to write: "*Some towns in the land of tightwad energy are not as big as this place. I gave the receptionist Tony's business card and told her that 'Dane' told me to stop by anytime, without an appointment, to just show the receptionist this card and wait to be seen asap. This is a pivotal point in my storyline, when I'll either find out Ray has a Fort Dodge Verla, or he just screws around with everyone, like T.P. thinks he does. Either way, my "T.E." story was headed for some kind of life-changing event in Verla's relationship with Ray. Like Crystal, I can feel it coming. I keep resisting the urge to write like my father did, inserting the whims of imagination into this real-life story. D. D. Wadstone was a craftsman who couldn't write about his life like I've been doing since I left L.A.; however, I'm still following his imagined blueprint of advice he left me in his writing crate, words that required action –he failed to take. So, I'm sticking with this story the way it is, no matter where it goes.*"

***

Dane was as friendly as any of my Tightwad Energy customers, buying and unloading 10 cases from my station wagon before I could sit down in F.D.I.'s massive '*Break Room*' inside the plant. I have this hunch that Tony called Dane about me in advance of my impromptu meeting. It was just too easy:

I'd walked into his office, and before I could sit down…he jumped up from his desk as if elated about this seemingly '*perfect timing*' to buy my product. He said he was out of 33-gallon liners, planning to get heavy-duty liners for his cans in The Break Room. Dane rode with me to the delivery door and helped me unload 10 cases without even asking me the cost. This had to be my first sales experience where tightwad energy…was missing. *Something was definitely out of balance here;* that was my train of thought while enjoying a free fountain RC and burger I picked out in the cafeteria that had no checkout-register. All soft drinks, burgers and dogs were free in this massive white cafeteria that looked like an empty grocery store covered with white plastic tables and chairs for the 3,000-plus employees coming and going through three separate doorways of hanging plastic slats I'd seen in small-town meat lockers in my territory. I wrote later:

"My $240 invoice was nothing to Dane. I gave him no break in cost; it was full markup, so I made $120 profit and watched him go from can to can removing old bags and replacing them with my product that Dane said was perfect for some of the crap that gets tossed in. He took my invoice over to payroll close by and I had a check within five minutes. He handed me my check and told

*me that he knew Ray went to The Pink Flamingo, a strip
bar he gave me easy directions to. For all I knew –Ray
could be there now with his Fort Dodge Verla. That's
what I thought as I entered the dark strip bar with Hazel
against my side; I was ready to say Ray Vining sent me
as I approached the bartender."*

***

Again: perfect timing. I found myself driving back to
Woodbury with all my inventory sold, since The Pink
Flamingo bartender, Gus, also bought 10 cases. I had
$480 in my pocket after 2 easy stops; and again, I had
this *feeling* that Dane had called Gus, the bartender at
The Pink Flamingo. That total absence of tightwad
energy outweighed my probing into Ray's personal life,
or the *other life* Tony believed Ray was keeping from
Verla. I had a good sales day. I'd like to sell all of
Ray's customers 10 cases at a time…as quick as
possible. I wasn't sure whether to ask Ray or Tony
about such a perfect list of prospects. I seemed to be out
of that tightwad energy zone of withholding, and knew
my next move had to be made now. I needed a cheap
cargo van, and Max Hermann would help me…and fast.

***

It started to snow these slow-falling big flakes on this
perfectly windless late afternoon on Hermann's dock. I
was staring at my new white cargo van while smoking a
cigarette I bummed from Joe, the warehouse manager for
Max, who was now filling my order for next week. Now
I can stay out all week, expanding my territory in this
land of tightwad energy my dad said *"would easily
stretch hundreds of miles in either direction."* Thanks to
Max, who called a wholesale auto dealer in Salix, I had

84

my perfect vehicle delivered to me within an hour for $1400. Now I could sell my station wagon to Klem, the old retired chain-smoking pharmacist who lived across the hall from Verla, who mentioned to me in the elevator that he was looking for a car for his girlfriend. I thought he was kidding, until early one morning when I saw old Klem getting out of a cab in front of Sammy's with a woman who had to be 30-something. At first, I thought it was his daughter visiting from Omaha…until I saw her kissing Klem at their table. Just then: Joe came out of the warehouse 2-wheeling 10 cases at a time until my 50 cases were on the dock.

I felt good about leaving my van parked in front of Max Hermann's dock overnight after calling my insurance agent and getting full coverage on my new van. Now I wanted to go see this furnished apartment I saw the other day that was only 3 blocks from The Argo. First, I cleaned out the station wagon, and put everything I wanted in the van. I figured if Klem didn't want to buy this old heap I could get $50 bucks for it tomorrow at the salvage yard across from Hermann's. I wiped the snow from the station wagon's back window and drove away from Hermann's dock feeling as if nothing could go wrong today. I was getting hungry and wanting to catch up on my writing. But first, I had to get my own crib. Ray was due for a visit. This midnight quickie stuff gets old.

Verla's Little Tiger

I did *not* want this day to end. I saw the perfect furnished apartment for me and filled out the application right there after seeing the place. The apartment was on the 2nd floor of an old Victorian corner house with a big garage for my van; the exterior paint is lemon-yellow with white trim like Verla's *Birdie*. Yellow was a good color for me; that's what Crystal always told me. She said the right Yellow girl would come along and force me to grow up...or I'd lose her. Another good sign on this perfect day.

My prospective landlord knew my *references*, Max, Sammy and Verla, and all but assured me I'd be approved quick. What a day: my easy big sales in Fort Dodge; a new van and apartment. No tightwad energy all day long. That was something my dad said he envied, *"when I'd see a man or woman every now and then spending their love and money so freely without the slightest concern about it returning to them."*

Snow kept falling softly without any wind when I parked in my parking space at The Argo...maybe for the last time. Verla's parking space was empty, which meant she was still at happy hour in Al's; or she could be waiting for the roads to be cleared for Ray's *visit*. Either way: I walked into Tommy's and told him about my new apartment and van, and how tomorrow was the last night I could do the dumpster duty. Tommy was so cool about it and said that he'd take out the dumpster tomorrow, since he knew I was moving into a new place.

Feeling lucky, I took the elevator up to Verla's floor and checked to see if old Klem was home. He wasn't. Verla's apartment was a mess: clothes on the floor, full ashtrays, dirty dishes piled up, the bed was unmade and there was this strong odor like gasoline in the apartment. So, I opened her big window and lit one of her Winstons from a pack on her cluttered bedside table after wolfing down 2 slices of cold pizza inside a carry-out box on the counter. Seated on the ledge in front of her open window, blowing my smoke into the soft-falling snowflakes...I was numb from this perfect day as nightfall approached. I didn't want to drag my dad's writing crate out to the station wagon since I planned on crashing in the back of my car tonight until Ray left. I got my bedding and pillow after straightening her bed, dumping the ashtrays, and tossing her clothes in the closet, including a bath towel hanging from the bathroom doorknob. Again, I knocked on Klem's door after dumping her garbage down the chute. He wasn't in.

***

It was warm and cozy in that station wagon. The last thing I remember before nodding off to sleep was telling myself how perfect today was.

***

I was so close to deep sleep and so comfortable with my head under the blanket...when I heard Birdie's engine

87

running then shut off. I hoped Verla didn't see me or couldn't see me in here when I heard Birdie's front door open and slam shut…and then I heard those familiar little feet in high heels hurrying toward the hotel's back door. I remember thinking that maybe Ray can't make it tonight because of the snow piling up and that's why Verla's apartment was a mess. Anyway, I went back to sleep, not wanting to leave my cozy little bed.

***

Next thing I remember was a *LOUD AWFUL THUD* on the roof of the station wagon that jolted me up from a dead sleep, causing me to bang my head on the dome light of the cargo bed. The glass was all frosted over. I scrambled out of the station wagon in deep snow to see what could've hit my roof.

"Don't move him!" Verla warned me, her naked body leaning out her 3rd floor window as I stood there looking at Ray's naked-white body lying on his back on the roof of my car in a bed of fluffy snow; his eyes were closed and his *little tiger* was still erect. He had to be dead…yet I didn't see any blood.

I really thought I was dreaming this…until Verla came out the back door wearing a black nightie with pink fuzzy slippers and her Ann Margaret wig with Ray's bundled clothes stuffed inside her purple blanket.

"Oh my God, Ray, is he alive?" Verla was beside herself.

"I don't know."

She checked his pulse: "He's alive!"

"Did you call the police?" I asked her.

"There's no time for that. We have to drive him to the hospital," she said.

Verla drove my car while we each held onto her purple blanket that covered most of Ray's body and his tent pole. It was amazing that his body didn't slide or move in that deep snow impression on the roof as Verla plowed through the snow to the hospital while obviously stressed to the max. This was the longest drive, going 20 mph through 3 red lights, yet we were getting Ray to the hospital faster than any other way without moving him.

I was the one to run inside the emergency room to get 2 men on staff to remove Ray from the roof and onto a gurney.

"He had a bad fall," Verla told the men after wrapping her purple blanket around her shivering body and tucking it into her bosom.

When the men had removed the blanket, there was Ray's woody standing at attention as they carefully lifted Ray's body off the roof and onto the gurney, wheeling him into the hospital. Verla handed me Ray's dress shoes and his bundle of clothes after getting his wallet and rental car key out of his pockets. She kept the key, went through the billfold, making sure there was nothing related to her inside his wallet before she gave me the wallet and whispered intensely into my eyes:

"I can't have a police report on this, Billy. Give them his wallet and clothes. You don't *know him* or *know* what happened. You found him on the street and drove him here...okay?"

I nodded in this stunned state of complicity that she demanded from me. Then she told me she'd be parked down the street a block, that she'd be waiting for me. She hurried into the station wagon and drove away.

I found myself walking with Ray's clothes into that florescent nightmare of lights, approaching the admitting area and knowing I was now an accomplice to something illegal, something that was big trouble for Verla and me. And I didn't even know what happened. I kept thinking she must've found out about Fort Dodge Verla, and that she threw Ray out her window...that I left open.

Stepping up to the admitting window I tried not to look like I was part of this cover-up when I mumbled to the admitting person:

"This is the man's clothes that were in the street. His wallet is in his pants. I don't know who he is. I have to go."

So, I left...even though the woman was calling out to me...I kept walking. Outside, I ran a block until I saw my idling car, where Verla was pushing the snow from the roof, removing any trace of Ray's imprint. I could see a visible dent on the roof.

Verla was shivering and had been crying; driving to The Argo she pounded her fist on the steering wheel and screamed:

"That cheatin' piece of shit gave me crabs!! I knew he was screwin' around!!"

I told her I just bought a van and that it's parked at Hermann's dock. She parked in my parking space, got a screw driver from Birdie's glovebox and told me to remove my plates and *toss 'em in the basement dumpster*. Verla went upstairs to get dressed as I removed the plates and threw them into the dumpster like Verla told me to do. *Is this real?* I kept asking my busy mind.

Soon, I followed Birdie downtown - with no plates - to the back of that old brick building next to Nort's bookstore where Ray's rental car was parked. Verla explained that Ray would park his rental car here and take a cab to her place if he'd been drinking and the weather was bad. I thought *at least he was drunk when he flew out her window.*

I stood there watching Verla open the rental car's trunk and remove Ray's leather double-handled sales case that she placed inside Birdie's trunk. When Verla was wiping off fingerprints from the interior of the rental car –I thought I saw someone looking down at us from the upstairs apartment window above the bookstore; that's where Nort and his scowling wife live. So much for not being seen by anyone. I didn't tell Verla about someone possibly seeing us after she purposely left the rental car key in the ignition.

I found myself (emotionally) on the couch, as if seated between my parents while they studied all those TV shows. Now here I was with Verla, a willing accomplice in this real episode of "Tightwad Energy" titled "Premeditated/Accident"; and I *wanted* to help her get away with whatever happened in her apartment. Like Raymond Burr in one of my dad's Perry Mason

91

episodes, I had to ask her, while she wiped her prints off both door handles of the rental car:

"Why would Ray leave the key in the ignition?"

"Because he'd be drunk and lose his keys," Verla snapped back.

"Why would he park *here*?" Again, I sounded like Perry Mason in one of my dad's scripts.

That's when I knew I was about to find out certain things, *things* that even my mom didn't know about her big sister. Verla stepped right up to my face, her little gray eyes stressed to the max, she pointed above our heads to a dark window on the 2nd floor of an obscure old hotel next to an iron fire escape:

"That's Ray's room. Ray and Jane bought this building when I first moved here. They opened a brothel…and later called it The Hill. They had one in Omaha and were expanding… T.P. and I became partners with them."

She stopped me from getting my notebook, telling me we'll go to Sammy's and she'll tell me what happened, "the whole crazy story, but *after* we clean out your station wagon, you leave it parked at the dock with your van. When the salvage yard opens tomorrow…"

"Sounds good," I said, following orders and sounding like Paul Drake, Perry's private investigator.

***

It only took a few minutes to clean out the station wagon; then Verla said she had to get some smokes. I was ready to smoke a pack of Winstons with her at

Sammy's with a pot of coffee. I was anxious to hear what happened, and how Ray fell out of her window.

What Happened

I didn't want to miss any words she spoke while she paced in Sammy's with the front blinds twisted shut. We were both still on this intense adrenaline rush ever since Ray's fall. She brought out this office lamp from Sammy's office so I could write up a storm on Verla's strong coffee and enjoy that Winston dopamine rush burning in a shared ashtray on our corner booth table, the spot where she always read my work. This time: I'm documenting her life, trying to get her words down, not some imaginary fictional character doing imagined things. I wrote her words:

"Ray came into my apartment. It was dark. I was in my sexy nightie and mad-ready for this liar who gave me crabs. I'd put on some extra perfume to cover that awful kerosene ointment. Anyway, I heard him undressing at the end of the bed. Right when he was ready I kicked him in the balls so hard...I didn't even see him fly out the window!"

I'd have her "*wait*" while I caught up with her words while she took these fast sips of her strong coffee and would light another Winston with the butt from her spent one and said with a shrug, "That's...what happened."

94

I could see she really cared about Ray and whether he survived or not; and she believed that my car - with all that snow on the roof - saved Ray's life:

"No bouncing or any blood, just flat on his back like a pancake."

Now I understood why Verla couldn't file a police report, because of her involvement in a brothel with Ray, Jane *and* Tony. Then there was that *big sale* she said Tony was trying to close.

Verla talked about the *early days*, and how Ray would come into Al's, where she was tending bar on weekends. He'd tell her about the money to be made in The Hill, that old 8-room upstairs hotel next to Nort's that Ray and Jane bought when Verla first moved to Woodbury. Anyway, Verla saved enough money working The Hill until her platonic friend and regular at Sammy's, T.P., proposed something in the same field, but on a much bigger scale.

I asked her earlier why we don't go down to the police station and we *just tell them exactly what happened.*

"Billy…a naked man with a boner fell out my window and might be dead because I kicked him in the balls for giving me crabs. This sale with Tony can't be messed with right now. Tony and Jane would agree…*and* Ray."

Then when I asked her if anybody else could've seen what happened, she stopped me with a stern tone, reminding me that I was getting rid of the station wagon first thing this morning when the salvage yard opens up.

* * *

Verla dropped me off a block from Hermann's dock and I had less than an hour to write in my new van; but with gas prices getting higher every day – it was back to the land of tightwad energy. No way did I want to sit in a freezing van or write with the engine running. Besides, all I could think about was whether Ray was dead or alive. I needed a distraction. Pinball at Nort's.

But first: I ducked into the old front entrance of The Hill that was boarded up. I'd asked Verla if the cops knew about this place, and she said they did, because a couple of retired city officials were known to be *regulars* over the years. Before going into Nort's I thought about walking to the back, to see if Ray's rental car was still there. Instead, I went through Nort's *tinkling* front door.

Nort's scowling wife was there behind the register reading a tabloid paper, and she almost smiled at me when I asked her for two bucks in quarters. Then came the first words she'd ever spoken to me, in her Polish accent she asked me:

"Is that Verla's car parked in back?"

It was shocking to hear her, and then to see her lips literally sneering at me in delight upon seeing my reaction of not knowing what to say…except:

"What car?"

"The car parked in the back. It's still there…go see," she pointed to the back of the bookstore. "I saw both of you there last night…"

"That's not Verla's car," I said. "It's someone she knows."

Awkwardly, I turned to head for the pinball machine and could see a man looking at a magazine; I felt certain I'd seen him in Sammy's before. More awkwardness.

***

Nine games later –I had to get out of there. I could not focus on pinball after Nort's wife said she saw us last night. I left Nort's walking fast, anxious to tell Verla about being seen last night. Up ahead, I could see a familiar man, an employee of the salvage steel business; he was inspecting my station wagon as if it were a used car on a dealer's lot. From here I could see the dent on the roof of the station wagon that Ray's body made. I walked faster.

Change of Plan

Verla had cleaned up her apartment and had lavender-scented candles covering the crab treatment odor. When I told her Nort's wife saw us last night…she went right to her pack of Winstons for that dopamine rush addiction my mom said my dad always chose to live with.

"Is the car history?" she asked.

"Yep. Done. They gave me fifty bucks for it. I had to show them my title and drivers' license. Everything went smooth."

"It's perfect timing you got that van…"

"I know! My whole day was going perfect like that…until Ray fell out that window."

"Good news! I called the hospital and Ray's in a coma, but still alive!"

"Really?" I was stunned.

I grabbed a smoke from her pack when she opened her window more. We both looked down at the roof of my van parked in my space, still awe-struck at how far that was for Ray to fall. We agreed that we both looked tired. As we smoked together, she told me she was

thinking about whether to move Ray's rental car or
return it to the rental car agency where Ray rented his
vehicles. When I asked her again about whether we
should go to the cops…

"No way. Look, I'm off probation. I got busted for
soliciting twenty years ago. That's when I quit that end
of the business. And that's when Ray and I started
dating. Ray and I were business partners who could mix
business with pleasure… until last night."

"What about Jane in Denison?"

"They were friends. They have a beautiful daughter.
Jane and Ray were never married to each other. Jane's
ex-husband is an executive at the packinghouse in
Denison."

"So, Ray and Jane have a daughter?"

"Nell. You'd like her. She's as smart as they come.
And they'll be contacting Jane and Nell soon, if they
haven't already. It's the cops and insurance dicks I'm
worried about…"

Then: Verla changed her plan from returning the rental
car here, to parking the car at this Council Bluffs motel
where Ray was known to stay. When I asked why:

"To throw them off," she said. Then I thought she asked
me if I'd follow her in Birdie.

Follow Marilyn

After filling Birdie's gas tank, I drove to The Argo and parked in Verla's space next to my cargo van. My new vehicle was loaded with fifty cases of product and my stuff from the scrapped station wagon. Later, I wrote:

"I was smoking a Winston after getting a carton for Verla, plus a full tank of gas for Birdie, her lemon-yellow, white-trimmed Fairlane I was going to drive when following Verla in Ray's rental car to Council Bluffs. The rental car was still parked by The Hill's back door with the key still in the ignition. Verla didn't want me moving the car without gloves. I wanted to ask Verla to show me the rooms upstairs where she began her other career, but the timing wasn't right. Then: there she was, I could hear her 2-inch heels coming out of the elevator and those fast, little feet clomping on Tommy's old tile floor. At first, I thought she was a hooker coming out of the bar in a red leather mini-skirt looking for a cab. I'd seen plenty of women like her in L.A. It was Verla in her Marilyn Monroe wig that Beverly sold her. Verla's vast collection of wigs in her closet make sense now, after telling me in Sammy's this morning about how she'd wear the same wig with every regular, and never show the real Verla inside The Hill.

That way, there would never be any awkward encounters outside The Hill with these men. Wigs were Jane's idea that Verla really appreciated. Jane and Ray started an 'escort service' in Omaha. The girls working for them liked the idea that Jane would buy them a quality wig they had to wear on every 'date.'"

***

I had to follow *Marilyn* to Council Bluffs, another river town like Woodbury. My mother and Verla were raised in *C.B.*, and as D. D. Wadstone wrote in one of his notebooks I found in his crate: *"C.B. and Woodbury are the biggest cities built on these magical hills that were once sacred Native burial grounds. One night, Crystal and I were parked in my car in the Loess Hills, this gem of a place we called 'our spot.' She was teasing me about being a 'tightwad' and I said, 'It's that tightwad energy we talked about in Sammy's when we first met. We all withhold love and money. It's in our genes. A dualistic brain believes it has to withhold to survive the next disaster.' Crystal looked at me and said that was the first original thing she ever heard me say."*

I could see Marilyn's red gloves open the trunk of the rental car, then remove Ray's double-handled leather briefcase and leave the key in the ignition. I drove Marilyn away from that motel and asked her why she brought the briefcase.

"It's got a bunch of personal stuff Jane and Nell should have. They're his only family."

***

Our ride back to Woodbury was this 90-minute string of hypotheticals covering all scenarios whether Ray lived or died. Somewhere in her diatribe she mentioned that I could move into my new apartment tomorrow, that the landlord called and said I was approved. I was thrilled for this good news, then it went away when Marilyn continued talking, now wearing rose-colored glasses and candy-apple red lipstick she'd put on while looking in her visor mirror after turning on Birdie's dome light. She talked all the way home. Several times, I had her stop talking and repeat stuff so I could recall most of it later for my book.

There was no arguing with Verla *or Marilyn* when she told me to drive to the hospital, because she had to see for herself how Ray was doing. I was trying to understand why Verla hadn't contacted Jane or Nell about Ray's *accident.* She said she *couldn't* report this to the police. I felt certain it had to do with The Hill, that obscure little upstairs brothel next to Nort's that Verla said was a great money-maker for "The Family." That's what she called this ever-growing circle of *family* related to this prostitution gig that was being revealed to me in doses of what Verla believed I could handle. It felt like she was holding back…until I could catch up in my notebook with this crazy new reality of Ray in a coma with a traumatic brain injury. Verla was optimistic about Ray's full recovery after calling the hospital earlier today and hearing that Mr. Vining was still in a coma and breathing on his own. *"A good sign,"* the nurse informed *"a friend."* And when the nurse tried to transfer Verla to admitting after Verla informed the nurse that her patient has crabs…Verla said she hung up on her.

Verla told me that Nort and his sourpuss wife (Anna) have a key to The Hill's back door, and, *"they get paid to look after the place. Don't worry about them."* I could imagine those tightwads Nort and Anna watching The Hill visitors coming and going from their windows at all hours and later cleaning up the rooms, these characters I found perfectly suited for such business. Verla said she only worked The Hill *on her back* for eighteen months before getting into ownership with The Family.

***

As I sat behind the wheel of idling Birdie, parked in the hospital's visitors' parking lot, I lit a Winston and watched Marilyn hustle into the emergency entrance where we had dropped Ray off. Even now, I can still *hear* that awful sound of Ray hitting the roof of that station wagon. That violent *sound* made me not trust Marilyn with Ray this late at night…after visiting hours. Another Winston…then I shut off Birdie's engine, removed the keys and opened Birdie's trunk, bringing Ray's sales case onto the front seat under the dome light. First thing I pulled out of Ray's case was this fancy metal-covered photo album with "S o M" stenciled and centered in red letters on the front. I wrote later:

"There were dozens of black and white headshots of young women wearing wigs that resembled the hair color and hairstyles of celebrities: The Liz Taylor, The Doris Day, Patty Duke, Marilyn Monroe, Linda Ronstadt, Jayne Mansfield, etc. Then: I stopped on the page of a woman wearing 'The Donna Reed,' the same celebrity whose picture was inside my dad's writing crate. These women were all attractive, different

*ethnicities, yet none of them really looked like the
celebrity of the wig they wore. Then I found a laminated
photo inside Ray's case; I recognized Jane from the bar
in Denison, and the attractive woman with her I assumed
to be Nell, Ray and Jane's daughter."*

***

I found myself alone on the 4th floor of the hospital. The
intensive care *waiting room* was empty, and nobody was
around. I ducked into the *intensive care unit* where I
saw Marilyn's red dress behind one of the curtained
cubicles. I could see comatose Ray was breathing on his
own with inserted IVs for meds and fluids; and there was
his woody, still standing up straight under a green
hospital gown. Verla was holding Ray's fingertips,
talking to both of us as I stood on the other side of the
bed. She started whispering, looking down at Ray's
unremarkable face, a face I really hadn't looked at
before. Again, I wished I had my notebook when this
voice of the softer Verla talked; it reminded me of
Crystal when talking to her *clients* during her master
chakra readings:

"The nurse said comas can last a long time, that the
average one lasts a month. The brain has to heal. He
could have long-term or short-term memory loss, the
nurse said. I hope you don't forget the early years when
we were strangers. I know I told you that you were my
first time. I meant…the first time with someone I
loved."

I watched her cry and had no place to look…except the
past; it's what a conditioned mind does when it wants to
run away from the present moment. I'd heard words like
that before, when my mom talked about the early years

104

with *David*. Even after the divorce after my dad moved into his apartment, I'd ride along or she'd let me drive over to his place to deliver a dish she knew he liked: goulash or *Crystal's Chili*. We both knew she was checking on someone she loved and cared about, wanting to see for herself that he was taking care of himself. He never was.

One time, we drove over to my dad's place, Crystal went up to the door, knocked, and no answer. She let herself in with a spare key he'd given her while I waited in the car. We didn't know if he was in a drunken depression or what we'd find whenever we stopped over unannounced. She came out 15 minutes later; I could tell she'd been crying. She told me that he wasn't there, that she *cleaned-up a little*, picking up the usual mess he'd leave.

Marilyn and I left Ray's intensive care bedside not knowing whether Jane and Nell knew about Ray. In the elevator, Verla told me that Jane would've called her by now if she knew about Ray. That's when Verla said she wanted to talk to T.P. about whether she should contact Jane and Nell. Marilyn talked me into crashing on her floor one last night before I moved into my new crib. I had pages of recall writing to do.

Big Red's Pink Disaster

Monday morning, coughing Tony came into Sammy's for his usual breakfast with the morning paper. Verla had checked the paper earlier, and still no mention of Ray. My aunt warned me about talking to T.P. about Ray in Sammy's. I just wanted to have a quick breakfast and hit the road. I was anxious to get back to work in the territory and get away from all this *Ray thinking* and tonight crash in a motel room where I can catch up on lost sleep.

Verla wanted to stay in my furnished apartment over the weekend. She said she felt "creepy" in her place ever since Ray's fall into his *boner coma*. I gave up my bed for her and was comfortable on the couch in the front room, even though sleep was not there for both of us. All we talked about was her life with Ray and this *business* they created. I had a spare key made and of course let her know she could stay at my place. She liked that option. I could now understand why she couldn't reveal certain things about her *family business*.

Not long after T.P. waddled into Sammy's with his paper, I heard him say to Verla, "Still nothing." Around Tony I acted like I knew nothing about Ray or the *family business*. Verla wanted it that way; and, at the time I didn't know that it was Tony who was holding back from letting the girls in Denison know about Ray. Verla said that *"Lay-low Ray"* was good at living under the radar, and purposely made it nearly impossible to find *any trace* of his whereabouts.

During my breakfast I noticed that Verla and T.P. stepped outside to have a smoke and private conversation near my van in front of Sammy's.

***

I was near Blair, Nebraska, just north of Omaha, *"A tough town to work,"* T.P. warned me when I left Sammy's. Yet, I was relieved to get away from all this *Ray stuff* that drained my energy all weekend. It felt like I was in a David Lynch movie, dark and grim with no happy ending in sight.

***

T.P. was right. Blair was tough. I thought I'd never get a sale; and I had never encountered so many tightwads in one place –until I drove further west into Nebraska's heart of tightwad energy in towns like Fremont, Wahoo, then Seward, where sales were so scarce I thought it was me. It was. These were the tightwads my dad wrote about and left in his crate for me to find.

At the end of an exhausting day I didn't want to get a motel in Seward because they skunked me. I drove south to a Beatrice motel and traded a case of bags for a nice room. I needed a good night's sleep and hoped that tomorrow would be better in this clean nice-sized town in southeastern Nebraska. Before sleep I did a little writing:

"My worst sales day ever: 3 cases of product sold. I was tired all day, mostly because these tightwads kept pounding me with rejection all day. I've been tired before and did alright, because sales energize me. Fatigue never helps a stranger sell anything in these towns my dad warned me about in his writing: 'There are clusters of towns where tightwad energy rules every dime spent. These are the rural places peopled by men and women of faith, and yet these same God-fearing souls withhold love and money as if it was part of their religion. My girlfriend, Crystal, keeps reminding me that we are all Spiritual Beings having a human experience. I lose sight of that every time I enter one of these towns I call The Tightwad Zone.'

One positive thing I have to admit after getting skunked in Seward: I met an old man at a café lunch counter wearing what I thought was a faded Nebraska Cornhuskers sweatshirt that was pink. On the back of the sweatshirt in white lettering: Big Red's Pink Disaster. I didn't feel like talking to anybody, even though I was doing well with my mother's 'thoughtless awareness' training after a piss-poor sales day when this codger started talking about Nebraska football, and, 'Devaney's the best coach Nebraska ever had.' For some reason I had to ask, 'What's Big Red's Pink Disaster?'"

***

Beatrice was a great town to work. The people were open to me and what I was peddling, making up for yesterday with several multi-case orders. Right off the bat I was getting easy sales and telling everyone about the book I was writing. I was able to ask every single new customer in this big friendly town if they'd heard about Big Red's Pink Disaster. That's when I had to be ready with my notebook, taking notes. By the end of the day, I had not only made up for yesterday –I had this incredible human-interest story I wanted to fit into my book…somehow. And I had no clue how to do that.

This was *my* find, something other than the Ray insanity that Verla created. She'd sucked me into this whirlpool of runaway negative thoughts of prison for my part in covering up Ray's "accident." Every single time I mentioned Big Red's Pink Disaster, I got such an incredible positive response –I felt this instant connection that stopped the negative *what-ifs* Verla and I had been perseverating on ever since Ray's fall.

I wanted to get another motel room in Beatrice so I could spend another day working in this town that was giving me more than garbage bag sales. Later that night, in another clean motel room that I traded product for a room, I wrote:

"Tomorrow I hope to meet this Big Red, a man who lives a few miles east of here; a man who had this brilliant idea to market a product that his father created. He sold this product to thousands of loyal Nebraska football fans. This was before Devaney made the Cornhuskers a winner and a national powerhouse in Lincoln. From my extensive notes I knew that Big Red was red-headed Jerry 'Big Red' Krum, the taller son of a local eccentric

109

dentist who had a pretty good practice going here. Dr. Cal 'Red' Krum patented this red toothpaste-like substance that maintained its red color on teeth for 24 hours, the same dominant Nebraska team color filling stadiums during home and away games. Then, after the Saturday game, simply brush away Big Red's Toothpaste in warm water. But then something went wrong: fans all over Nebraska who'd bought the toothpaste left it on their teeth too long after game day, which stained the teeth a pinkish color that could only be removed in a dentist's chair. Dental bills and lawsuits brought Dr. Krum to bankruptcy, forcing him to sell his practice and hang himself in the family home Jerry was forced to sell. Today, Jerry supposedly lives alone east of town in a trailer behind a gas station he manages. I want to talk to this man...for some reason. I think it's related to this book I'm writing, to become this published writer my father failed to become. I believe in this story...and it's real...just as this Big Red must've believed in his father's product. Fiction isn't real. I've seen fiction destroy my father. My mother always told me 'nothing real can be threatened.' I don't want to end up publishing this real story and end up like Big Red, sued into the poor house."

***

A miracle happened in Beatrice: a nursing home here bought all my remaining product my very first call this morning. My biggest sale ever. The purchasing agent is a writer, and she told me she'd buy multiple copies of my book when I publish it. She laughed when I told her the title.

After a great lunch and no product to sell, I found this sign company in town who gave me a good deal on my van's vehicle lettering for $200. By early afternoon I now had "Tightwad Energy" in green and yellow lettering on both sides of my van, the same look and colors I wanted to have on the front cover of my book. T.P. said I don't need to put any other text besides that on the van. I trust his advice.

***

By 2 in the afternoon I parked at one of 2 gas pumps at Big Red's Gas & Scram, and filled my tank, amazed at the increase in gas prices of late. Big Red wasn't in. I didn't need to talk to him, for I could already see what the *pink disaster* had done to this man. The whole place was filthy and the old fart at the register looked all but dead…like the stinky old dog sleeping on the mud-stained floor caked with imprints from customer footwear.

After paying for my gas I walked around back and saw a beat-up pea-green trailer with a big man's work clothes hanging stiff in the wind on a clothesline next to the dumpy trailer. I'd seen enough of this guy. Now I could make it back to Max Hermann's dock before 5 and load my product for tomorrow. I didn't feel good about leaving Verla alone when I left town. I needed to see how she was doing; and, I welcomed sleeping in my own bed in my own apartment…if Verla wasn't there. Sunday night, Verla asked me if she could read any of my dad's stories in his writing crate. When rummaging through the crate, looking for something for Verla to read, a story to take her mind off Ray –she picked out one of my dad's Twilight Zone Episodes, "The

111

Watcher." I thought of that story while on my drive back home when moving alongside one of those endless 4-engine freight trains hauling coal across Nebraska from Wyoming. When my dad wrote it in the 60s it was way too far-fetched for anyone to imagine, except me; I had read it in my room in Culver City after getting stoned not long after my dad died.

The Watcher

I would hear Crystal talking to her clients in our home about *the dualistic mind* most of us have, including me. It's a mind that believes we are all separate egos; the ego loves that, my mother would often tell me, my dad, and of course her clients. Ten thousand times she told me to pay attention to my thoughts. And for a while I would, noticing this ineffable positive difference in my daily life. But then: my father would get another rejection for one of his scripts. My dad showed me and my mom this cynical one-word rejection that arrived on a tiny piece of paper the size of a fortune cookie that was paper-clipped to my dad's query letter submitted to an agent for a Twilight Zone episode, "The Watcher": "sorry." At first, when he showed this curt response to us –we all had a good laugh. But then: my dad would disappear, only to return home drunk and angry at the world. I'd hear my mom consoling him, talking to him as if he were one of Crystal's clients:

"You're allowing your mind to run your life. Your mind is not who you are, David."

Then, I'd hear my mother going over the 2-page query letter with him, suggesting changes here and there. The episode took place in 2044 when Earth leaders of government and industry were destroying the planet by this unconscious exploitation of earth's resources, mainly by burning fossil fuels. It was a challenge to breathe; children had to wear oxygen masks to school. One day, a spaceship appeared, hovering over the United Nations Building in New York. Military fighter jets were scrambled and zapped out of existence by beams of light coming from this alien spacecraft. A message was broadcast from the aliens to the leaders of the world inside the U.N. telling them that this planet was an experiment...that failed. They said that thousands of years ago *their* planet - in another galaxy - was also nearly destroyed by these same greedy elite and their appointed political leaders. The aliens explained that the worker slaves rebelled and sent the exploiters to Earth thousands of years ago, spreading them out evenly on every continent. These aliens then told the U.N. that they were to select only one man and woman, worker slaves from each continent to form a Universal Court who would prosecute all the political, business and religious leaders they deemed responsible for the greedy exploitation of Earth. These offenders would be stripped of their power and wealth and put to work repairing the damage done. Their wealth would be used by the worker slaves to repair the planet's ecosystem, thus accelerating human consciousness into a united planet with no boundaries.

***

Then: closing in on Omaha in my new *Tightwad Energy* van, soon to be crossing into Iowa, my mother's words to my father were clear:

"David, the primary cause of your unhappiness is never the situation. It's your thoughts about it...your mind's conditioned response going back to your early years in Omaha."

Soon, I could see the Loess Hills on my right as I drove north on 29, the same stretch of hills where David and Crystal met in Woodbury, and where D. D. Wadstone wrote that he would return to - if he was young again - to realize his life's work to be a validated writer. It became *crystal*-clear to me that if my book was real and good enough to make a positive impact –I'd have to destroy my father's conditioned mind that I chose to take on; and, that I must be *the watcher* of my thoughts, catch the quick lies about the dead past and imagined future...or I too will live an unconscious life that only validates the planet's collective insanity. Ray's fall is changing me.

First Impression

After loading my van at Hermann's dock, Tony parked his wife's car beside me and remarked that he liked my green and yellow vehicle lettering. Then he asked me, "What happened to Verla?"

"What do you mean?"

"She didn't come to work today or call in. That's not like Verla. Sammy couldn't reach her all day."

I got behind the wheel of my van; all I could think about were those sleeping pills I'd seen in Verla's bathroom medicine cabinet and how tired she was when I last saw her. Before I drove away from the dock, Tony came over to me and said:

"Just tell her the meeting is set. That'll cheer her up."

"The meeting's set," I repeated and drove away from the dock.

All the way to The Argo I kept going over those words my mother used to tell me about negative and positive thoughts, how scientists have proven under a microscope that negative words distort water molecules into discordant shapes compared to the clear beauty of water given only positive words. And since we are 70% water… I didn't feel good about the shape Verla was in when I last saw her.

Birdie wasn't parked in Verla's space at The Argo, so I drove over to my apartment, relieved to see her car parked in my garage. I ran up the stairs to my apartment while my fear-ridden mind showed me the image of my dad on his knees hurling into his toilet, his face flushed red with pain as now my hand trembled unlocking my door. Before opening my door...I knocked...knowing she wouldn't be expecting me back so soon. Then: before going in –Crystal's words were there, a gentle reminder to stop my thoughts about the imagined future and the dead past.

"Verla?"

I didn't see her in the front room; I saw her Doris Day wig hanging on my bedroom doorknob. Again, I called her name. Nothing. She was on my bed under the covers when she answered groggily, "Yeah."

"I sold all my product and came back to re-load. You don't feel good?"

She sat up and wrapped my covers around her naked body, then asked me what time it is. I didn't answer right away. My little bedroom smelled like the stifling spent breath of Scotch that I'd smell in my dad's apartment. I opened my bedroom window and knew she'd had a few drinks last night, because she had to be drunk to not open the window all the way.

"A little after five," I finally answered, shocked by her matted hair that was wet from perspiration.

"I'll have to wash your sheets," she chuckled a bit before reaching for a butted Winston in the ashtray on the floor that she lit quick when I said:

"Tony said you didn't call-in sick…"

"No… I couldn't sleep in my place… I closed the bar with Tommy," she giggled and explained her behavior by telling me, "Jane and Nell had Ray sent to Denison in an ambulance."

"A hospital in Denison?

"She waved me off, obviously hung-over. Then she explained, "I had to sleep in. First sleep I've had in days, Billy. I should've had Tommy call Sammy for me…but I forgot."

"Tony said to tell you the meeting is set."

"Really?" she looked at me.

"I just talked to him at Max Hermann's."

What a transformation: Verla got to her feet, butted her smoke and ran into the bathroom as if she'd just heard the best news of her life. Soon, I heard shower water running. I wanted to know about this *meeting*, and soon *heard* Verla shouting-out the toxins from last night, a ritual I'd heard before and usually after a long night of partying with Ray. She told me it was something she did "to get things moving" whenever she abused herself with too much to drink. Just then: on my kitchen counter I saw my dad's 2-page query letter for "The Watcher," the fortune cookie *"sorry"* still clipped to the top of the letter. A Twilight Zone coincidence I thought until I hurried to my Dad's green and yellow writing crate, lifted back the lid…and still there, in its place, was the fresh beautiful face of Donna Reed's original picture I'd re-taped to the lid; and I could tell my notebooks had been moved. My first thought was that she had read about Fort Dodge Verla, the imaginary lover that might've given Ray and Verla crabs. I imagined her reading all the things about Verla and Ray I'd written; and I could smell the smoker hands that had held my writing, that same smell whenever my dad let me read one of his stories. The things that Tony said, about not trusting Ray to be loyal to her, she had to have read. Then: I realized right there while looking into that 60-pound pile of fiction –my story is real; and it must've hurt Verla and sent her into a drunken stupor, adding even more pain since Ray's fall. *"Stuck negative energy,"* Crystal called it.

By the time the water stopped in the shower –I knew she felt better, because she was singing. She was *putting on her face* when she called out to me from behind the closed bathroom door that she was starved and wanted to go somewhere special to celebrate. I told her I'd be right back, that I was going to move Birdie and park my loaded van in the garage.

"I have no clue where my keys are!" she laughed.

After moving my van into my garage, I parked Birdie in front of the garage door. I opened Birdie's trunk…and Ray's sales case was still there. I looked inside the case and took one of Ray's business cards and read it: 'Sisters of Mercy/Mapleton, Ia./Ray Vining/toll-free #'; there was no address on the card. I put the card in my pocket and right away I was conflicted whether to ask Verla about the card.

***

We had a steak dinner at Marino's Steakhouse across the river in Nebraska overlooking the Missouri River. For some reason she talked about all the traveling she wanted to do, "see the whole frigin' country," she laughed. When I asked her about this *meeting* T.P. was talking about:

"I can't tell you anything about that, Billy, until sometime afterwards."

"After the meeting?"

"Yeah," she said, and changed the subject by asking me if I wanted to see the place where I was conceived.

"How do you know where I was conceived?"

"I'll tell you when we get there," she laughed before asking me if I brought my notebook.

***

Verla drove me and Birdie to the house where I was conceived, a one-room studio in a boardinghouse with shared bath that Verla rented for my mother soon after Crystal graduated from high school. I did my best to keep up with her in my notebook:

"Verla had my attention when she told me that prostitution is sex-for-money with a stranger, and that my parents were relative strangers the first time they had sex on their first date. That's how I got here. I looked up from my notebook and realized it wouldn't do any good to describe this place...because it's not the same place now: the old hag landlady who enforced curfews for the female tenants was dead; everything

about the place was the dead past. It was Crystals' first time, and I guess to some degree that makes me responsible for you being here, Verla said, even though David had to sneak through Crystal's window. Verla was making money 'turning tricks' and wanted her baby sister out of that awful environment Verla ran away from. Verla said she feared having children; she found that out when her strict foster mother took her to a gynecologist because she found out Verla 'was late' and wanted to get her on the pill before she got pregnant. She also let me know that all the girls working as Sisters of Mercy used protection to be safe from STDs. The point Verla made was that humans are going to have sex even if the people around them believe they shouldn't; and that one way or the other we all pay for everything.

I know now that Crystal and David ran away to L.A. to get away from these unconscious humans who raised them to believe in sin and guilt and a thousand other things that destroy young hearts and minds every day in this mind-made hell of the collective ego. Verla is aware that she reflected the insanity of her reality. Ask the Earth, the plants and animals; they're all aware of it too.

Verla gave my future parents three thousand bucks to pack up and start a new life in L.A., where my dad could be close to Hollyweird for his writing; and Crystal could be in a more liberal-minded place to do what she was born to do: help people connect with their spiritual oneness by quieting the busy mind. Verla reminded me that when Crystal was a little girl, Crystal said Jesus spoke to her in a dream, telling her to use her talent to heal others of suffering. My parents taught me to believe that Jesus was a spiritual teacher who saw the

121

world suffering with the fearful mind and was eventually tortured by this same collective insanity that threatens the planet today. My mother reminded my father more than once that it wasn't the Jews that killed Jesus, it was the collective insanity of fearful minds. Just the other day when selling on my route I met a veteran of the undeclared war in Viet Nam who told me he was afraid to burn his draft card with his friends because of what his family and others would 'think.' He said most of his buddies in the service felt that way; and yet, he said the politicians and the elite who never served in the military, don't have to face that kind of mental torture. The reason I got off on this tangent is because Verla told me that T.P. served in Korea and approached Verla, Ray and Jane with this business venture he came up with when he was facing death in Korea every day of his tour. Verla said that Ray liked T.P.'s idea and came up with the name, Sisters of Mercy, a business that allowed Jane and Verla to get off their backs and into management. My aunt said she couldn't tell me anymore about Sisters of Mercy until after this meeting Tony had just set up.

Before Verla drove us away from this place, she explained how T.P. was a mentor and father figure she needed in order to get away from selling her body. Verla was sincere when she told me that she knows what she's done to make money is considered shameful and wrong by the so-called moral majority, and that what she's about to do will only be more of a temporary fix for herself and her family."

After closing my notebook, I sat there on Birdie's front passenger seat with nothing more I wanted to ask my aunt. Soon, Verla drove me back to my place; she was excited now to clean her apartment and return to work tomorrow knowing Tony's impending meeting was about to change her life for the better. When I opened Birdie's front passenger door she said she wanted me to do her a favor the next time I worked Denison:

"What?" I thought I asked.

"Can you drop off Ray's briefcase? I don't want to be around Jane or Nell until this meeting is over. There's a toll-free number on Ray's business cards. Just call that number and Jane or Nell will meet you and pick it up."

I said I would, not wanting to tell her I already had one of Ray's business cards in my pocket. She turned off the ignition and handed me her keys and said, "It's in the trunk."

"How soon do they want it?" I asked.

"No hurry. Next time you're there."

***

I put Ray's sales case on top of my dad's crate in the front room of my apartment and tried to forget it was there, resisting the urge to empty its contents onto the floor. Then the noise started in my mind. I'd heard it before, many times in school and most days after my parents moved into separate bedrooms in our home. That's when I started looking forward to Saturdays more and more, when Crystal's clients would come and the noise in my head would stop. My dad resisted it, staying in his room, not at all wanting to be around these loving people he called, *Crystal's sprout heads*.

Now I can see clearly that my parents' separation was a split between light and darkness. It was easy to see on Saturdays and most difficult to bear as the week went on. I found myself looking forward to Saturdays; instead of getting away from our house that seemed darker during the week because of a man who resisted inner peace –I would welcome these people who brought love and light into our *space*. And it was Verla that made all those Saturdays possible. Thanks to my mother and her big sister...I would get to see this light of peace –until the darkness I inherited from D. D. Wadstone took over...as it always did.

My eyes stayed on Ray's worn double-handled leather sales case standing on his tomb of dead stories I've chosen to drag around this land of tightwad energy, all for this man I *have to love* for sneaking into that window, that window of safety my aunt provided for her baby sister. I had to ask myself if that night of passion was only to create me and run away together, far away from this place my father wrote about and left for me in this crate of darkness. I emptied Ray's sales bag onto the green crate, ready to find the next chapter that Verla seemed to be helping me write.

David and Donna

Early Thursday evening I parked in the Denison hospital parking lot after a tough sales day in the heart of tightwad energy. All day long I was unable to stop thinking about what I'd found in Ray's sales case. I wanted to see for myself how Ray was doing after he was transported here by ambulance earlier this week. I resisted the urge to call that toll-free number on Ray's business card. Like calling on a new prospect –I wanted to surprise Jane and Nell when I delivered Ray's sales case to them.

An hour ago, after dinner, and after trading a case of garbage bags for a room in the Denison Inn, I showered and put on my best clothes, wanting to make a good first impression. Fear of the unknown was in my head as I sat behind the wheel of my van. So many questions I wanted answered for my book; and it was clear to me I couldn't ask Verla anything about her *business*, since she was holding back any further information until *after* that arcane meeting T.P. had set up.

I had to do something my father never did on his typewriter: take over the story by doing *real* research. But first: my inner fear of the unknown had to be vanquished, and the only way to do that was for me to follow Crystal's advice I'd heard her give to hundreds of clients over the years:

"Live in a state of Zen. Pay attention to every breath and feel the energy inside your body. Keep that attention on every step you take…and be aware of space between thoughts. Be instead of do."

And there it is: Ray's sales case, standing up on the floor of my van next to me. I grabbed the handles in my right hand and felt the old worn leather on my fingers before getting out of my van and locking the door with more attention than I've ever given such a trite thing since leaving home in L.A. Fearful thoughts would come and go so fast —I could only catch them if I stayed in the present moment.

I was there, on the Denison hospital parking lot, each step slower on this concrete slab poured onto this rural piece of earth on the eastern fringe of those Loess Hills, the very place my father wrote about in his notebooks. All day long I had moved from one prospect to the other…into my head…a means to an end that my mother said was collectively destroying any real chance of inner peace for billions of people. I asked myself: *Why isn't this simple way of 'Being' taught to busy minds in schools all over the planet? Memorized rote learning about things, all academic tests that bored me to no end…couldn't help me whenever I'd leave my divided home and enter the space of a thousand other minds racing with ten thousand fears coming and going from every direction.*

Fearful thoughts about where my story was headed would come and go.

Stop it! I ordered that voice in my head that was so fast –
I could only catch it if I gave it my full attention...then
let it pass by.

Every step, I felt, on that vast stretch of concrete
poured over this rural space of land so close to those
same hills my father said he would return to –if he was
young again. I had to get off this concrete to a spot
where I could be alone, because my mind kept showing
me images of anything except the present moment.
Once my feet hit the frozen snow-covered ground of
winter...I stood still with my eyes closed...seeing that
awful time in Spanish class my senior year when it was
my turn to stand up and say something in Spanish to the
class...and to the teacher, *Val,* my mother's lover. No
words would come...Spanish or English... Only this
siren of fear blared in my head...as now...until I was
able to *scream* at those dark hills:

"*Why* are you doing this to my father? He knows you
come to our home every Saturday to be with Crystal!
That's when I *feel* him *dying* behind his closed door,
writing his fictional stories to keep from *thinking* about
you being with the girl of his dreams!"

Across those hills I could imagine that Hollywood
magazine photo taped to the lid of my inheritance; I
caught myself holding my breath...feeling the same
white-hot anger now running through me here on this
patch of frozen ground...just as it had when I sat back
down at my desk and wore the mask of a boy
unafraid...a boy who simply hadn't learned his lesson.
My classmates giggled, and my ego was saved when my
teacher (Val) protected me by saying nothing and
moving on to the next student. Now: I breathed again,

seeing the magazine shot of Donna Reed inside my father's crate, this *dream girl* of my dad's imagination who once lived close to these hills in the land of tightwad energy, her photo still taped inside that wooden tomb of lost words. Then: I could feel the handles of Ray's sales case still in my hand. Inside it: black and white pictures of dozens of women, these so-called Sisters of Mercy, all disguised in the wigs of celebrities; a list of a dozen packinghouses in a dozen cities and towns scattered across the Midwest, where Ray Vining peddled his escort service. The names and phone numbers were all there, hundreds of executives who paid hundreds of dollars for being with one of these women for one hour while billing their massive Chicago-based corporation for aprons and knives and gloves.

I knew what D. D. Wadstone would do: he'd play it safe, holed-up in his office, pounding the keys on his typewriter until another story was ready for his crate, another unsold episode of *Perry Mason* or *The Fugitive*…lost forever.

I started walking, paying attention to each step with Ray's bag-of-boners along for the ride, closing-in-on this rural hospital's emergency entrance some 200 yards away. My book had to continue. That was my motivation.

***

Within 15 minutes I walked out of the hospital not at all surprised that Ray Vining had never been transported here from Woodbury. The intensive care RN assured me that no comatose patient was in this hospital. I had to imagine what D. D. Wadstone would put on the next page of his story, and so I drove back to my motel room in Denison. Scenes flashed across my mind, things and words that David would do and say…if he was young again. All kinds of images came to me while driving back to my room until I parked my van directly across the road from the motel in a Dairy Queen parking lot.

In room 16, I paced out my next move as I'd seen my dad do a thousand times when working out his stories. I put Ray's case on the bed and his business card on top of the phone's receiver, looking at them while pacing back and forth across the room…talking out loud any possible scenes and dialog. I knew I was in my head, thinking about my options; and, what D. D. Wadstone would put on this page. Every scene made me more and more anxious, especially the ones when a Sister of Mercy knocked on the door of this room.

I was so desperate –I went Crystal's way, the way of *Being* that she preached to me and my dad, and to those *sprout heads* who my father and I both knew were paying our bills…and yet –I followed his ego and resisted with him. Zen was Crystal's way of slowing things down by doing one thing at a time with full attention on every little thing, including every breath as I walked over to the window, felt the stiff curtain on my hand when I swept it open and watched conditioned thoughts race across my mind so fast. Most of it was fear, about what could go wrong…and questions: *Why would Verla leave Ray's case with me and have me deliver it to Jane and Nell when she must've known I would look inside it? Why let me see those photos of those women and those bogus invoices signed by their customers all over Ray's territory? Was it because of my book? Was Verla leading my story down a path she wanted me to follow?*

129

That same negative energy that blocked my father's aliveness…started to move in waves of electricity around my skull while I remained still…until Billy was there.

"This is *my* story," I whispered to the winter night before moving purposely over to the bed and I sat beside Ray's *bag of tricks,* removing the notebook list of executives, customers of this *escort service* alphabetized by location. Then: I picked up Ray's business card, and before my mind could stop me…I dialed the toll-free number, ready to be in control…like David was when he made all those phone calls from his office.

After 3 rings, a young woman's voice was clear and confident:

"Sisters of Mercy…may I help you?"

"This is David. I work at Fort Dodge Industries. Dane referred me… I'm in Denison."

I stayed quiet…waiting for her response:

"Your account number, please."

I looked at the number beside *Dane* in Ray's notebook and repeated it:

"Six eight zero three."

Another pause…until she asked me if this was for tonight.

"Yes."

"Where are you staying?"

"The Denison Inn."

"Room number?"

"Sixteen."

"David…who will be your celebrity date tonight?"

"Donna Reed."

"David, does an hour from now work for you?"

"Yes," I thought I said.

The voice hung up. I don't remember hanging up the receiver. Then: I looked at the red numbers on the clock on the bedside table: 9:27; I sat there stunned at the same numbers of my dad's birthday, September 27th. I got up and went to the window again, not at all conscious of my steps this time, just like my dad would do…since he lived in his head most of the time. I could see my van was parked where it should be, far away from the room, like any customer of this service would do…if waiting for *Donna* to show.

David's mind was there…in me…as if in the throes of a full-blown Twilight Zone scene…racing toward a *climax* that even Rod Serling could never imagine. I'd never really had sex with a woman, not really; it was awkward and meaningless the few times I was with any girl in L.A. My heart raced with the passing seconds and then I looked back at the red numbers: 9:33.

Again: I had to go to Crystal. I resisted the thought to call her in Mexico. I had to get out of this cage so I could walk and breathe. I grabbed Ray's case, and left the room, not even sure if I locked the door behind me.

Talk To Me, Dad

My busy mind missed the snow falling until I reached the white blanket covering my van's windshield in the D.Q. parking lot. Awareness was lost. The snow only reminded me of the same white powder that most likely saved Ray's life the night he fell onto my station wagon. I put Ray's sales case in my van and locked it again, needing to walk and figure out my next move before my date with *Donna*.

I walked east alongside the main road...away from the town and facing light traffic coming into town. Again, I took Crystal's way, stopping fearful thoughts by giving my full attention to feeling and *hearing* the *crushed snow* underfoot mixed with the occasional *slicing slush* made by passing vehicles from both directions. Then: I'd take my father's way, allowing my mind to show me the fear of a nearing carnal experience with one of those women in Ray's photo album.

"Research," my dad would say.

Then came the voice of my mother from behind their closed bedroom door, gently urging her husband to stop his suffering with these fictional stories his mind made up, a mind that had totally convinced him that when he sold one –he'd be *somebody*. I'd *hear* her reminding him of the early years and how that he was not the man she fell in love with. *"Come back to me, David,"* I'd hear her cry to him. He never did. His ego was buried so deep inside his pickled brain…neither Perry Mason or Dr. Kildare could save him.

Now: I paid attention to Crystal and kept my awareness on every breath of cold air taken from this land of tightwad energy…until again I went back to the dead past before they separated, when she told him he was lost in the madness of his male-dominated stories that Hollywood wanted, and reminding him again that he wanted to change Hollywood with his stories. *"Talk to me, David,"* she pleaded.

Soon, I'd *hear* a door slam, then the *sound* of our car driving off into the city night…to be with like minds who agreed with him. Later that night, I came out of my room and saw the light was still on under my parents' bedroom door. I went to the fridge for a swig of juice out of the bottle and saw one of the many affirmations Crystal would put around the house: *"A relationship is to make you conscious…not happy."*

Now: I stopped in my tracks…and turned back to the town of my dad's *dream girl* who'd left this very place and made it big in Hollywood. *"Was Donna your motivation, Dad?"* I whispered into the cold air, imagining the stretch of whiteness covering the earth to be the blank page D. D. Wadstone had faced a thousand times…and failed. My busy mind was there:

Talk to me, Dad. Help me with this scene. I'm writing it for you. Where would you take me from here? I want this insane world who rejected you a thousand times to read it and see that your life was not wasted, Dad. I can't finish it without you... What should I do?

It's Your Dream

I t had to be close to 10:27 when I saw a new black
Mercury drive onto the motel's snow-covered lot
and park near room 16. From behind the wheel of
my idling van in the D.Q. lot, I was the son of a
screenwriter who could imagine my cleared windshield a
movie screen where I watched a woman in a hooded
full-length black coat and matching gloves get out of the
Mercury and knock on room 16's door. Soon, *Donna*
knocked again; then she looked around at the parked
vehicles nearby…returned to her car…and she waited a
while in her idling Mercury until she backed away. Her
headlights flashed into my eyes before she drove back
the way she came. I waited a bit…and followed her.

***

It wasn't long before I knew I had to get back to my
room, before the snow left me stranded, since I didn't
have snow tires. No way could I sleep now; first, I had
to write down what I'd experienced after tailing that
Mercury:

*"Following that Sister of Mercy was like one of those
Perry Mason episodes stored in my dad's crate. I felt
like Paul Drake, Perry Mason's private investigator who
uncovered clues and evidence for the case Perry always
seemed to win. I stayed far behind the Mercury heading*

west then northwest about 11 miles; then Donna turned west onto a rural road a few miles before Mapleton, a scenic little town I'd worked and knew to be on the eastern edge of Loess Hills. I kept vacillating back and forth from Crystal's self-awareness of breath and body to the busy mind of a screenwriter fleshing out the details of a scene. It was a balance of mind and no-mind I seemed to need so that fear didn't drive the story all the way to the end. I didn't dare get close enough to read the license plates that Paul Drake would've gotten; instead, I was in the throes of what I knew my father would've told me: 'It's your dream.'

It scared me when that Mercury turned left onto that rural road before Mapleton and headed west into the darkness of those hills where concrete and light vanished on a road so remote there were no other tire tracks to follow —except that Mercury's. Instead of turning onto that road where my headlights would give me away...I waited a bit...until all I could do was follow her fresh tracks so I at least would know where to come back tomorrow afternoon after working Denison; and by that time this road might be cleared of the snow piling up. Time...the ego always wants more of it. Between that split-second swishing space of clarity of my windshield wipers...I had to keep switching from David to Crystal, from mind to no-mind in order to keep my mind's conditioned fear from rising up from my belly and wanting to send that old negative energy to my head...where it could run me off the page...as it did with David, sending him to his delusional fix of smoke and alcohol. Crystal helped me stay alert by keeping my attention on my shallow breathing while following the fresh tracks that soon would be covered by this heavy snowfall, destroying the evidence Perry needed to make his case. The tracks turned into a one-lane drive up a steep hill. I stopped to see the lights of a house on the right at the top of the hill. On my left was a mailbox. My headlights revealed no name on the box. I had to back up and get back onto the road without backing into a ditch. Once I was positioned to drive back the way I came...I stayed parked there on the road, a void of darkness ahead and behind me. I asked my dad again what I should do: walk up there, knock on the door and say 'I'm David from room sixteen, but not really; I'm really Billy Wadstone...I followed you here because I'm writing this book...and are you a Sister of Mercy?'

Now, here I am, back in my motel room, anxious to work Denison tomorrow before the next chapter."

Donna's Place

Friday's sales were terrific. My repeat customers bought bags for friends and relatives who wanted to save a little money and still get quality. They were referring me to businesses in town who'd heard about me, this garbage bag salesman/writer from Woodbury they wanted to meet. T.P.'s sales tips were paying off…in a big way.

The day flew by so fast, barely a spare second for my mind to dwell on my last stop before heading back home. But first: I had to write things down that were coming to me faster than David Jansen could get out of town. I couldn't tell if it was Crystal or David who told me to go into Donna's place now to write these things down. Something inside me was shifting. I'm not sure it will last.

***

"I stepped into the sparkling-clean nostalgic soda fountain shop with Ray's sales case holding my notebook. There were several pictures of Donna on the walls. I'd resisted calling on this place, and I didn't now as I bought a root beer float and sat at a window table facing my favorite town in the land of tightwad energy. It was obvious to me that the owner of this place

*loved Donna, for every inch of every picture frame
holding shots of her career on these walls –had a light of
wholesome goodness about it that was missing in most
places I'd experienced.*

*And there: standing on the chair across from me at
my table was Ray's old leather sales case that held the
list of Ray's customers that must still live in this area:
Slick Willy, Lefty, Fast Freddy, Dead Eye, Sleepy
Hank...and dozens more; all of them executives of the
massive corporation that owned dozens of subsidiaries
that supported towns like this one. Some of these men
had to be married, examples of the collective dualistic
separation from God we're all responsible for. And here
I am, as self-centered and hypocritical as any of those
boners in that bag...worried about finishing my book
and writing about these Sisters of Mercy customers who
support the very businesses who support me and buy my
product.*

*Seated here in this place, seeing the image of a
woman this whole town must have watched with delight
every week...gives me hope that good things will come
from a story that will only offend those readers living in
their heads all the time, closed minds who believe they
can't learn anything from a woman like Crystal. Time
and again I heard Crystal tell anyone who'd listen, that
all great spiritual teachers talked about Source, God,
Creator, Great Spirit, whatever name that you want to
label it –all of them knew that most suffering comes from
the conditioned mind and separateness. The mind keeps
us all separated and the suffering continues. We all see
it every day. Going back and forth from my fear-
conditioned mind to no-mind is my biggest challenge
every day of my life. I see that so clearly now. Coming*

139

here, playing my mind games with this book I'm writing...ends Now."

Nell and Jane

I parked on that same rural road not far from the mailbox near the entrance to that lane that led up to the A-frame, a newer building that I could see on the right at the top of the lane perhaps a hundred yards or so from me. Too much snow to drive up there. I had Ray's case in one hand and a case of garbage bags I held balanced on my shoulder as I headed up the hill. The busy mind of a storyteller was there between my ears, but this time –I noticed it: *Should I look inside the mailbox for mail? If anyone asks: How did I find this place? Did I look inside Ray's bag? Is that picture of Ray and the little girl with red hair that I found in his case, Nell?*

Climbing that hill, I put my attention on the nature around me, as I would back home whenever Crystal would send me on an errand or when walking to school and back home after school. It was easier to do that here, where there was no concrete or smog, or those obnoxious sounds of a city that I'd become numb to. Here, there was snow covering trees, the flitting wings in flight and *sounds* of birds, and the crushing *sound* of snow under my shoes –all of it a meditation that my mother begged me to experience…while I was young.

As I'd trained my fearful mind to stop thinking about what I would walk into when calling on new customers…there was the black Mercury parked on the other side of the A-frame. I stepped onto the horsehair 'Welcome' mat, the exact same one in front of Max Hermann's office door. T.P. came to mind; that's when I was able to stop any thoughts about what I would say to anyone who answered my *knock* after putting Ray's case down and onto the mat while holding my product on my shoulder. Right when I picked up Ray's bag –the door opened a few inches and I saw a young woman, half-asleep as if awakened from a nap. For some reason I knew this was the Sister of Mercy in the Mercury; I could *hear* a Rare Earth song in the background and smelled jasmine mixed with a tinge of cinnamon incense when I asked her:

"Are you Nell?"

"Who are you?"

"I'm Billy Wadstone. My Aunt Verla wanted me to deliver Ray's case to Jane and Nell."

She looked at the bag in my hand and told me, "They're at The Home," she pointed to my left, then added, "You'll see it if you follow that trail."

Before I could turn back to her and say thanks…she closed the door. There were no tracks in the snow to see or follow this trail. I was glad that she wasn't Nell. Verla told me that Nell was Ray's biological daughter, and that Jane was once married to some *big shot executive* at the Denison plant, who I knew was one of Ray's customers on his list I found in his sales bag.

Step after step I tried to stay out of my head; my mother taught me not to judge people or label them anything…for any reason my mind could come up with. Not far from the top of the hill, I put down Ray's sales bag and switched the case of garbage bags onto my other shoulder then turned back to the A-frame, whereupon I could now see a large deck on the other side of the A-frame that overlooked the open space and panoramic view of the hills my father wrote about in his notebooks.

At the summit, I could see what looked like a large single-story brick apartment building a few hundred yards down into this valley maybe 200 yards from here. There were construction vehicles parked near the building and I could *hear* electric sawing and hammering coming from inside the finished exterior. From here, I could see that there was a road leading back to the same road where I'd parked, an easier route I knew I'd take after my delivery.

There was a new silver-colored T-bird parked near the main entrance of *The Home* as construction *noise* intensified. Through the front entrance glass near the double doors I could see painters at work in their white paint-splattered work clothes finishing the white trim on the lavender-colored walls. There was an oval-shaped nursing station that reminded me of ones I'd seen in retirement homes. That's when I first thought: *Could Ray be here?*

A challenge was upon me: I knew that if anyone had called Dane at Fort Dodge Industries…they'd know it was me, Verla's weird nephew who had his own agenda. If Verla called to let them know I'd be coming, or if they asked how I found this place –I'd be a snoop working for Perry Mason, never to be trusted by Nell or Jane, two new characters in my book that had a story to tell that could make or break me with my readers. Yes, I was my dad, into my head again, lost in one more meaningless fictional plot that was destined to end up sealed in a box with a thousand other characters that nobody cared about. Verla seemed to believe in my book, and *why would she lead me on about that by having me deliver Ray's bag-of-boners to women who exploited men for sex and money?* All this mind stuff was draining me now, as I could feel the pinch of pressure on my shoulder from the weight of 250 garbage bags while moving down the right wing of this place, where the noise of workmen was far less than the sounds coming from the left wing.

There, the first open doorway on the left-side of the hallway, where I stopped…and I could see comatose Ray, his tent pole still standing under his green hospital gown while breathing on his own in a hospital bed with EKG equipment, IVs, and catheter tubes inserted as if he'd never left intensive care. When I stepped into the room with my delivery, I could see Ray was wearing white TED hose up to his knees and *snoring*. I didn't recall hearing him snore the last time I saw him. To the right was an open door that led to an adjoining apartment, furnished, with the good aroma of chicken soup that reminded me I was hungry. I went to the adjoining apartment and knocked on the wall without looking inside.

"Anybody here?" I called out.

Soon, a woman, (who had to be Nell) with red hair, faded jeans and paint-splattered white sweatshirt came into view after I backed up from the doorway. I saw her look at Ray's bag and her mint-green eyes softened behind the lenses of her red-framed glasses. I would guess her to be around 30 years old.

"Are you Nell?"

"Billy?"

"Yes!" I said louder than my ego wanted to.

"I'm Nell," she smiled and took Ray's bag out of my extended hand. I brought the case of garbage bags down to my chest and told her this was a house-warming gift from Tightwad Energy.

"I saw your van parked in Denison today!" she smiled again as Jane came into view, the same woman I'd seen in the bar with Ray when I worked Denison for the first time with T.P. "Mom, this is Billy, Verla's nephew."

"The writer!" Jane exclaimed. "You're just in time for tea and my homemade chicken soup, Billy."

"Great," I thought I said, and stepped into a furnished apartment that reminded me of the room I stayed in last night.

Nell took the case of product from me and told her mother I brought them a case of garbage bags.

"That's so thoughtful," Jane said and told me to sit down at the table and Nell will serve me some tea.

"You like ginger tea?" Nell asked.

"Yes. My mom always made tea."

"Didn't you move here from L.A.?" Nell asked.

"Yeah, Culver City."

"I lived in Westwood," Nell said.

"You went to UCLA?"

"Until I dropped out," she laughed and sat down next to me after serving tea while Jane served me a plate of cold veggies and a steaming bowl of chicken soup.

Like most people who live in their head most of the time, I was a different person enjoying this impromptu meal with Nell and Jane. Then Jane surprised me when she asked me how my book was coming along.

I was curious and asked Jane, "Did Verla tell you about my book?"

Then, I lost my presence when Nell answered for her:

"We *all* know about your book."

"It's coming along," I said without wanting to talk about it; while my mind bothered me with thoughts of what I'd written about Sisters of Mercy, and how they must know that I was Dane, the voice on the phone that stood-up *Donna* last night. I changed the subject.

"How's Ray? I don't remember whether he was snoring or not the last time I saw him in the hospital."

Both the women were excited, and Nell let me know that he just started snoring a couple days ago, and, "It means he's waking up. The swelling in his brain is going down."

I wanted to ask them if any doctor explained why his tent pole wasn't going down. Considering their *business,* I didn't ask, for fear that they'd bring up *Dane's* phone call and no-show last night.

***

I listened to the women talking about The Home and a thousand other things I had to recall for my missing notebook. My mother taught me how to listen by keeping my attention on my life energy with every breath whenever I was lost in my world of thoughts. Then Nell gave me a tour of The Home, showing me all 8 apartments, 4 on each wing of the building with 2 apartments connected on each side of both hallways like a hotel room. All of them but 2 on the other wing were ready for occupancy. When I asked the women *who will live here*, Nell's curt answer busied the same plot-point mind of D. D. Wadstone I'd seen pacing in his office for hours at a time: "The Family."

***

I turned down Nell's offer to give me a ride to my van, telling her I felt like walking. Actually, I was feeling gassy from my root beer float earlier and needed privacy, away from Nell, this woman that was maybe 30 and out of my league. It was good for me (and Dane) when Nell hugged me goodbye and said they looked forward to seeing me next time I'm working this area.

Walking down the private road that was recently plowed, I knew I had thousands of words to get out of my head and into my notebook. I felt better about this Sisters of Mercy service that at first appeared to me to be nothing more than a seedy escort service that would be illegal in 49 states. There was so much I learned about *The Family* from Nell and her mother. I could see in

Nell's mint-green eyes that she was (logical) smarter than me and comfortable in her skin, not at all unconscious as I am most days. All the way to my van it was meeting this Nell that made me stay present, seeing the natural beauty of my surroundings without trying to label them as this or that. Then: other things would come into my head, like the tender care I observed both women giving their snoring patient. Nell would talk to Ray when checking his vitals, in this soft tone that relaxed me, she whispered: *"Ray, you can wake up when you're ready. Verla's nephew, Billy, is here."* Then she asked me if there was anything I wanted to say to Ray. I said, *"Hi, Ray... Verla says hi...and that she's sorry about what happened."* Then, frail Jane was at the foot of Ray's bed putting lotion on his feet after removing those TED hose and massaging his feet; and like Nell, she talked to Ray as if he could hear her, *"Can you wiggle your toes for me, Ray?"* No movement at all from Ray, only the sound of *snoring,* deep and loud as if he really could wake up from his traumatic brain injury...just to be with these women who truly love him. I could tell they loved him far beyond this mundane world of greed and money, when they told me that Ray's life insurance policy doesn't pay if suicide is the *likely* cause of death; and they were both so understanding after talking to Verla and how she couldn't file an accident report. I liked these women.

She's Yellow, Mom

F riday night and most of Saturday I stayed away
from Verla, and so I was able to catch up on
things I needed to put in my book, things Nell
and Jane revealed to me. While writing, I was
clear about one thing regarding Nell, something I had to
call Crystal about, something only Crystal could
confirm. My Saturday call began with my mom telling
me how well she was doing with her readings in Mexico,
that she was getting more and more Americans living in
Ensenada as clients; and, that Val was supporting her
more than she'd ever been supported by anyone in her
life. Then I told her about Nell, that I really like her,
and:

"She's Yellow, Mom."

I asked her about the best way for me to handle a Yellow
master chakra. I listened:

"You can't reach Yellows with your heart, Billy. Stay
ahead of her by staying out of your head…or you risk a
loss. Are you still in Green?"

"Green-Blue, lately."

"Uh huh."

"Remember that woman who came to our house with rainbow tattoos on her arms?" I asked.

"Rachel."

"Yes! I thought of Rachel right after I met Nell."

"Yes, Rachel was a raging Yellow then," Crystal said. "Well Billy, if Nell's a Yellow master, you both could prosper in business together. It could be a dynamic union that way; and Yellow is your best possible sex partner…at first. But the sex wears off, trust me," she laughed, reminding me how her laugh used to sound when my parents were young and still happy together.

Then: Crystal revealed to me things she knew about Green and Yellow together in a relationship:

"It's best if it's business *only,* especially if she's *older* than you," my mom seemed to know this about Nell. "She's a thinker and she'll always be a step ahead of you. Yellows remember *everything…*so you don't have to. They can be extremely mindful and they balance it with creativity. That's her attraction to a Green like you. She needs you to stay present, out of your head, because that's her field. Otherwise you're just another man with an ego she'll compete with…and win most times."

"Nobody wins mind games, Mom."

"That's right. That's the world. She plays in the world much better than you ever will."

Without talking about my book, Ray's coma, or this Sisters of Mercy business, I had to ask her:

"Mom, you told me Verla was a Red when she was younger. I feel like she's Orange now."

"How so?"

While I was having trouble explaining with words, astute Crystal knew how to get it out of me when she asked if Verla had a recent emotional disturbance.

"Yes! Very much so," I said.

"Was it a love interest?" Crystal continued.

"Yes."

"Was there anger on her side?"

Instantly I could recall that awful *sound* when Ray's naked body fell onto the roof of my car.

"Yes! Lots of anger," I said.

There was a long pause between Ensenada and Woodbury as I was anxious to hear these words of truth that nobody else could give me about Verla. Then, Crystal's words rang true when she said:

"One of Verla's traps...if she's in Orange...she'll punish herself for this emotional disturbance. Billy, it's nearly *impossible* for a Red who moves into Orange to move-on emotionally...until she forgives herself for her part in this disturbance."

"Is there anything I can do to help her, Mom?"

"Love her through it. She won't listen to anybody except her guilt-ridden mind. Just love her through it, Billy."

151

"Okay."

***

Early Saturday evening, after doing laundry and writing at least three thousand words that Crystal inspired—I decided to walk over to The Argo with my notebook, knowing I had more to write after my visit at The Home. I was in my head about what I'd written last night and after talking to my mom today:

"I found the 'chakra chart for relationship chemistry' my mother gave me, that I keep in my dad's writing crate. It confirmed everything Crystal told me today; and convinced me that I had to stay with this story Ray had helped me fall into, because there are no accidents; and —because I really liked The Family who had nearly completed The Home, an isolated retirement home where Verla, Tony, Jane and Ray could live independently during their golden years. I couldn't get past the fact that this was a good cause for long-term care for these people. Each of the 4 owners have their apartment and each one had an adjoining apartment for visitors or live-in caregivers hired by The Family trust that Nell set up five years ago when she joined 'the business.' My thoughts kept returning to my book and how Verla didn't tell me much about Sisters of Mercy earlier. It must be related to Ray's life insurance policy that wouldn't pay if they knew he'd been kicked out of Verla's window or a suicide attempt. That nagging background question: 'How can I sell my book to my customers when Sisters of Mercy customers were all living and working in these very same cities and towns?'"

Again, I'd lost my awareness to my busy mind, finding myself standing near the back entrance of The Argo, looking up at Verla's window…then down to the roof of Birdie parked on my old parking space. The distance Ray had fallen amazed me and reminded me that I had good news for Verla about Ray. I knew Verla's patterns, that she could be in the bar here…but I wanted to see her apartment, since I could tell how she was feeling by seeing her living space.

I took the musty stairway, whereupon I could smell that pest control must've just sprayed recently. On the 3rd floor I could smell the second-hand smoke coming from Klem's open dormer, knowing he brought his Sister of Mercy girlfriend here every Saturday night ever since The Hill was shut down and out of business because of this big meeting T.P. was supposed to have any day now.

I knocked on Verla's door. No answer. I used my key to her apartment and could see that she was depressed: The Murphy bed was down and unmade with clothes scattered about and dirty dishes with full ashtrays reminded me of Crystal's words about her sister's *emotional disturbance.*

***

Her back was to me; Verla was sitting alone in the bar downstairs at a booth, her empty whiskey and Coke glass and a burning Winston on her ashtray reminded me of Jane when I first saw her in that Denison bar with Ray. She heard me order a Coke from Tommy at the bar and called out to her landlord, "Put that on my tab and hit me again, Tommy!" I saw the double shots Tommy gave his favorite tenant, and knew she was depressed whenever she drank whiskey and Coke. I asked Tommy discreetly how many she's had. Tommy put three fingers down on the bar and I knew there was something going-on with her. When I sat down across from her she asked me if I met Nell and Jane.

"Yes, I did. And I saw The Home. But first, I have good news…"

Her sad eyes widened a bit, when she said, "What?"

"Ray's snoring," I leaned forward and pulled one of her Winstons from her pack.

"You're kidding?" she started to cry tears from what I thought was pent-up guilt Crystal talked about.

"The doctor said it's a sign he's coming back."

She kept crying into her chubby hands, swiping away her running mascara, she said, "My God, that is good news."

"What's going on with you, Verla?" I asked.

She took a deep breath and told me that T.P.'s meeting with the packinghouse big wigs was cancelled.

"How come?"

"T.P.'s got lung cancer," she cried into her hands. "It's advanced…too far gone for surgery or chemo…"

"When did you find out?"

"Yesterday when he got back from the Omaha Cancer Clinic. That crazy bastard came into Sammy's tubed-up to an oxygen tank he wheeled in…and he lit up a Camel right there at the counter… He's pissed at me now."

"Why?"

"I dunked his pack of smokes in his coffee…and he left."

After more complaining about T.P.'s stupidity, I told her I called my mom.

"How's she doing?"

"Great. She and Val are doing well. She said to say she loves you."

"My Crystal baby," she sighed lovingly. "What do you think of Nell?"

"I like her. I had lunch there, in the apartment next to Ray's room. She gave me a tour."

"I haven't even seen the place since they started construction."

"Really?"

"Yeah, I don't want to see it until it's finished. I know Nell will get that place done right. She's amazing. She's the one that made our service take off."

"How's that?"

"She screened all the sisters for zero hard drug usage…and organized the service like nobody's business, Billy. That girl is one smart woman, *believe me*."

"Oh, I believe it."

***

After getting Verla to bed in her place, I walked to Sammy's, and was able to write about a chapter in Ray's life that Jane revealed to me.

Ray's Pal

"**G**etting to know any family brings understanding. Jane wanted to tell me something about her early life in Denison with Ray. Jane and Ray were about the same age and raised within a quarter-mile of each other on family farms between Odebolt and Denison. Their fathers were close friends and neighbors their entire lives. One day, Jane's father asked Ray's father if he'd do him a favor, a task nobody in Jane's family wanted to do: put down the family dog, Pal, an Irish wolfhound that was dying of old age and suffering under a corncrib. Ray's dad told his friend he'd send 12-year-old Ray over to put down the dog. Jane said, she can remember seeing Ray walk over to the corncrib with his rifle, and that her father had dug a hole behind the corncrib, showing Ray where it was. Jane said that even her father couldn't be there, since Pal was a good farm dog and was older than all his kids. Jane said the whole family watched Ray from the porch windows, all of them crying as they heard the shot of his rifle and watched him drag Pal out from under the corncrib and carry him to his grave.

Years later, Jane and Ray ran into each other in a bar in Omaha where they were both living, and Ray told Jane that besides her father, nobody in her family talked to him again after he put down Pal. It was as if they held it against him for something he was ordered to do. Jane told Ray right there that she was sorry and that she never realized that her family never did let Ray know they understood what he had to do, and that there really was never any conscious hard feelings against him. Then: Jane and Ray started dating. Soon, Ray confessed to his girlfriend that he started drinking not long after putting Pal down, and that he was lost in guilt for so many years."

After writing this episode in the lives of Ray and Jane, I realized there was so much more to learn about these people who created Sisters of Mercy –because of their lives. I looked up from my favorite writing table where Verla had read about my life, my story, and I could see so clearly this carnival of characters in Sammy's. Some of them regulars, old men and veterans of past wars I'd talked to, and how they too were ordered to do things that I could never even imagine. They too have their stories. And each one of them could fill a thousand pages about the people in their lives who helped make them who they are now. Except: they don't know that their past is not who they are. They've chosen to listen to the stories in their minds, over ten thousand days and nights of the same broken records playing over and over…not even aware of it. It's insanity. It's the insanity we've all allowed the minds of others to make us who we *think* we are. Where are the conscious women who can stop this madness? Men can't do it;

their egos won't allow it. Something has to give.
Women have to take back their power.

Violet Ray

April-cold rains soaked into the deepest soil on earth, onto the Loess Hills that stretched from Woodbury to Missouri. This sweet air was new to me, far removed from the acid rain splashed onto L.A. concrete that always reddened my eyes and kept me indoors most of my life.

Now, nearly 2500 Tightwad Energy customers were ready to buy my book whenever I published it. Purposely I'd worked every town within 50 miles of the Loess Hills in every direction, even Missouri towns like Maryville and Rock Port. They all kept buying my *dream product* while I now pounded away on Herman, taking my dad's typewriter into motel rooms, where I was typing (what Verla read) for Nell and a small publisher in Omaha who did everything from editing to cover design. Nell wanted to be my 2nd reader –before she submitted my first few chapters to Diane, a friend of hers she referred me to, who would give me a fair quote and a quality product that I'd verified with several small-town presses in my territory.

Nell was giving me such good advice. Just as T.P. had helped me become a better salesman, Nell suggested I get my price per copy (what I could get) from my future readers, which she figured would be around 12 dollars per (signed) and delivered copy. She also said I should keep an alphabetized list (by location) for every customer. She even offered to put my list together for me if I could provide a copy of all my customers; plus, she ordered the Library of Congress copyright form I'd have to fill out before I published my book. Yellows are perfectly suited to run a business, and Nell was a true Yellow if I've ever seen one.

My no-show date with Donna was never mentioned by Nell or Jane. The Sister of Mercy who showed that night was Kate from Omaha, who stayed at the A-frame. I met her (for the 2nd time) when Nell and Jane invited me to dinner a month ago. That's when I found out Tony's cancelled meeting was about selling the *service* in order to get out of the business for good. I still didn't know whether Nell has a boyfriend, or if she would even consider a younger Green like me. All I know is that *The Family* treats me like family…and I like it.

***

By Saturday I'll have my first notebook typed and copied for Nell and Diane to read. Nell was going to personally drop off her copy to Diane after she read it and gave me feedback. I'm anxious and excited to have Nell and Diane read my work, two people not related to me. Honest feedback can be painful, yet I was now more determined than ever to publish "Tightwad Energy" even if they think it's not ready. When I asked Jane and Nell about Sisters of Mercy and their customers being in my plot, both women said that a new meeting with the same buyer would be scheduled soon and that Sisters of Mercy would be history anyway. Nell then called her attorney and was told I shouldn't use any of

161

the real names of their clients (for legal purposes) to be safe; and that it would be best to use fictitious names for all my characters. It was good timing to know that, since that was the first thing I had to know before I could start up Herman's engine. My first *novel* will be born soon. I wish my dad was here to see it.

***

I went to bed early for a Saturday; I was tired from typing on Herman, having reached my self-imposed deadline to have my first notebook typed and copied for Nell to read before taking it to Diane, who would give me her estimate for printing 5,000 copies of my novel. About the time I was into deep sleep –I was rudely awakened by a *loud pounding* on my apartment door. I rolled out of bed and behind the door was Verla's frantic voice:

"Billy! Open up!"

Upon opening the door, she burst inside wearing her Liz Taylor *beehive*; she was dressed for Saturday night, squealing into my half-asleep face:

"Ray came out of his coma! He's back, Billy!!"

"What?"

"Hurry and get dressed! T.P.'s downstairs waiting to drive us to The Home!"

I don't remember getting dressed, grabbing my typed pages for Nell or leaving Woodbury in Tony's wife's car that was already cluttered like the old station wagon he sold me. The whole trip was unreal: Verla talked non-stop while our driver smoked his Camel with

162

oxygen tubes inserted and his oxygen tank standing on the front seat next to Verla, who poured me a cup of strong coffee from T.P.'s thermos into a Styrofoam cup in a plastic sleeve T.P. had me find on the back-seat floor. I sat in back listening to these two old friends and absolute control freaks; they were talking about this *miracle* that happened earlier this evening. Jane had called Tony, and Tony found Verla on a barstool in Tommy's. I wasn't sure why they wanted me to ride along until Verla asked me if I brought my notebook. I didn't. All the way to The Home, Verla was obviously in her head about what Ray's reaction to her would be after waking up from his coma. Tony made the mistake of asking her, "Why are you so *whacked-out* about seeing Ray?"

Her beehive, an inch from the car's roof, *Liz* turned to bark at her driver:

"WHY? You ask *WHY...*after I kicked him out of my *WINDOW* and into a *COMA?"*

Calm Tony, always the salesman, tried to calm her down with his positive spin:

"You're the *one* who got him to the hospital. He'd be *dead* if not for you."

"That's true," she agreed and looked back at me to see my agreeing nod.

"Besides that," T.P. continued, "if Nell can get that meeting re-set...Ray will be a millionaire and he can retire in Mexico like he always talked about."

Verla didn't say anything about Mexico, although I've heard her talking about how she and Ray could live in

Mexico like her sister…if they ever get enough money to stay down there.

During this quick-flash drive to The Home, I kept thinking about Nell and how happy she'd be right now as Tony and Verla talked over each other's words. My last visit to The Home, I'd met briefly, Ray's physical therapist, Roberta, a big German gal from Harlan, who would soon move into the adjoining apartment next to Ray's room. Afterwards, I'd walked back to the A-frame with Nell, on our way to have dinner that Jane prepared. That's when I asked Nell if she's always called Ray by his name. I wrote later that night what she said:

"I didn't know Ray was my biological father until I was in high school. And yet, somewhere above any words, I knew he was my real dad. He'd always be there during holidays. He'd bring me gifts. And I really liked him."

I asked her about her ex step-dad, Bob, being one of Ray's *clients,* one of the first executives at the Denison plant to get involved with Sisters of Mercy. That's when Nell added insight into these lives of the characters in my book who became more than flesh-peddlers for greed. During this same walk to the A-frame, Nell said that her mother got pregnant by Ray just before Sisters of Mercy, and that she became involved with Bob before she knew she was pregnant, about the time Bob was promoted to plant manager. Jane and Ray remained friends, and Bob was an easy-going guy who played the role of Nell's father as Jane and Ray wanted. When Jane and Ray, along with Tony and Verla, pitched their Sisters of Mercy *service* that was already off and running in 3 locations around Omaha –Bob was open.

Nell said she was kept in the dark about their business until she was enrolled at UCLA, where during her freshman year she had roommates who were *working* the same kind of escort service to pay for their tuition.

Nell was a true Yellow, a thinker and researcher who wanted to drop out of school and make Sisters of Mercy more professional and organized. And she did. When I asked Nell, what would become of the *sisters* when they sold the business, she said they would go back to their regular lives as if the past is dead, and that all of them were aware of the approaching end of their escort service.

***

When Verla, Tony and I arrived at The Home, we entered Ray's apartment...and there was Ray Vining, angled up in bed, his tent pole was down, and his lit gray-green eyes didn't recognize us, even Verla. Nell and Jane were there; Jane told us he hadn't spoken yet, and Roberta, his physical therapist, told Nell and Jane earlier that Ray could get back his memory...or not. We all watched Verla step up to Ray's bedside. Verla could see that there was *no Ray there* when she looked into his eyes that were clear and lit with light she'd never seen in his eyes before. Verla cried until her mouth began to tremble with the same grief-stricken face I'd seen earlier when Ray was in the Woodbury hospital. Nell, in a tone so rare for a Yellow, explained to Verla:

"Verla, he can't understand you. His doctor was here earlier and told us he's like a baby who has to learn from scratch...even potty-training."

Verla composed herself, touched Ray's hand, then stepped back from Ray's bed, soon turning away from us to sob uncontrollably while Tony stepped up to Ray and patted his arm before stepping away with his oxygen tank following. That's when Roberta came into the room to feed Ray his first solid food since his fall, a jar of banana pudding baby food.

It was obvious that *The Family* loved Ray, and all were grateful to have him back. Jane and Nell invited us to the A-frame for coffee, which we accepted. As we started to leave Ray's apartment, Roberta gave us hope when she told us that she's seen many patients come back from comas longer than Ray's with all their faculties restored…including their long-term memory.

As Tony followed Jane's Mercury to the A-frame, I knew that Orange Ray was now Violet Ray. I'd seen many Violets in our home every Saturday, clients of Crystal who were re-born spirits of light in a middle-aged body. Yet Ray was this empty vessel of stillness that only Nell and I seemed to recognize from our experiences in L.A. We both knew this stillness in people as a good thing that most people are unable to sustain for long in a world dominated by busy minds filled with noise and insanity. From what I'd seen at Crystal's Tea Club –Ray was conscious for the first time in a long time.

Blind Spot

Ray's awakening from his coma energized all of us in this pre-dawn casual business meeting Nell was leading in the comfort of the A-frame. I managed to stay in this same quiet state of awareness that Ray was in while seated on this beige horseshoe sectional sofa that faced the expansive deck and view of the Loess Hills. Nell began reading good news from notes on a clipboard, informing Tony and Verla that *sisters*:

"Ginger now works full-time in a hair salon in Omaha as a partner. Beth Ann is now office manager in her uncle's construction company in Dakota City."

I found out later from Verla that half of these *Sisters of Mercy* were employed elsewhere; and, that the *service* has been out of business for 2 weeks, ever since Nell arranged a meeting with the corporate board of directors in Chicago. This was good news for Tony and Verla, who knew that Nell had taken over for Tony after his serious health issues were diagnosed. Nell also proposed a doubling of the selling price to the buyer, whereby Verla and Tony were now asked by Nell to vote *yes* by raising their hand. Since Nell was Ray's appointed executor and Jane already approved of the increase…both Tony and Verla voted in favor of the increase in the sale price for their *escort service.*

Observing this *Family* - all seated around me - I was back into the stillness of Crystal's Saturdays with her clients. All of them, including Nell, were thinking about what more money would mean for each of them, since most of the original selling price was earmarked for a trust fund that would provide long-term care for them in The Home. Tony stepped outside onto the deck to have a smoke with his oxygen tank rolling beside him, whereupon Verla joined him as Jane was busy preparing a pre-dawn breakfast for all of us. Nell went into Ray's room after knocking lightly on the door; she told me that Kate - the visiting *sister* I'd met - was catching a flight back home to Oregon later this morning, and that "*my boyfriend*" is giving her a ride to the airport. Right away, when Nell told me she has a boyfriend, I felt this energy rising from my belly. I recalled what Crystal did and watched this rising energy without resisting it; it was the same white-hot energy I felt when I watched my father lose Crystal to Val. I had internalized my father's pain of losing the love of his life, the *Donna Reed* image who had run away to L.A. with him to start a new life…and become somebody. I was aware that Nell was watching me when she returned to the sofa after waking Kate –yet I didn't care. This was too important. I'd seen Crystal do it a thousand times, giving her clients space; she called it a *blind spot,* a trusting presence that allows stuck energy to move, to dissolve these negative past experiences that I only noticed within me whenever I'd been close to Nell.

"Are you okay?" Nell asked me.

"Yes, I'm fine," I laughed a bit.

Then: another challenge came right away in the form of a *knock* on the A-frame door…before it opened. Nell hurried to her feet to greet her boyfriend arriving for breakfast before he drove Kate to the airport. There he was: this smiling handsome young man, dressed like a farmer in an old baseball cap with worn jeans and flannel shirt. I heard him remove his boots before Nell brought him over to meet me.

"Billy, this is Paul."

I stood up to shake Paul's powerful rough hand before he sat down with Nell on the sofa.

"Paul's a farmer," Nell smiled at her boyfriend.

I caught it: My mind tried to label this couple *Ray and Jane.* I stayed with this new energy inside me that was not making me uneasy as before. When Nell bounced up to get Paul a cup of coffee:

"You're that writer, the Tightwad Energy guy," Paul smiled at me.

I nodded positively and he told me that's such a cool name for my business, and:

"How'd you come up with that name?"

"My dad gave it to me."

His positive nod was enough for me. No story needed, since now it was easy to be here, my thoughts not coming at the usual speed. Paul was not at all self-conscious. We both sat there in stillness, even after Nell

169

brought his coffee. But then: Verla came inside from the deck.

"Is this the *mystery boyfriend*?" Verla surprised the young farmer.

"This is Paul, Verla," Nell smiled at her boyfriend.

"Hi, Paul!"

"Pleased to meet you, Verla."

"Such a gentleman, and good-lookin' to boot," *Liz* winked at Nell.

Verla sat down next to me when Tony came in with his oxygen tank; T.P. forced a smile after Verla made a cynical comment about his smoking. Then Jane told us breakfast was ready and we all sat at a circular table in the dining area, including Kate, who had taken a quick shower before getting dressed for her flight. During breakfast, Nell asked me if I brought my first chapters for her to read. I told her they were in Tony's car.

"I told Diane I'd drop them off to her this week," Nell said.

That's when Verla went on and on about my writing, and how much she enjoyed it, and that my father wrote *TV shows*. Kate asked me what shows she might've seen. It was awkward to tell everyone at the table that he never sold any of his stories.

***

After breakfast, Paul and I loaded Kate's luggage into Paul's truck. Nell kissed Kate and her boyfriend goodbye and we watched them drive down the lane.

"You feel like going for a walk?" Nell asked me.

"Yeah, that sounds good."

Not U

"**L**oving caregivers are Violets like Roberta," I said to Nell while she led the way on our walk along a narrow trail that ascended to and followed this tree-covered ridge overlooking The Home.

She laughed at my *"chakra talk"* she said she'd heard a thousand times when going to school in California. I made that comment after she asked me what I thought of Roberta, Ray's powerful German physical therapist with huge hands perfect for massaging atrophied muscles. I knew better than to talk chakras with a Yellow like Nell, who has no use for anything unless backed by sound proven research. Yellows are all about facts and bottom lines.

I managed to stay in this state of thoughtless awareness, until she commented on Ray's woody, how it went away when he awakened from his coma.

"Verla said he was always that way, ever since she's known him," I said.

Then I asked Nell if Paul knows about Sisters of Mercy."

"He thinks it's a massage service for executives. That's what we tell people...*if* they ask."

No thoughts came to me; I was able to keep my attention on these sacred hills indigenous people chose as burial grounds for loved ones on their way to the Great Spirit. I wrote later this evening:

"There was something about Nell she'd been withholding, something I felt certain would show up on the pages of my book before the ending. Like with her boyfriend, Paul, a mystery revealed. My challenge is to stay out of my head about it, to go with the flow until the book is finished.

Returning to the A-frame, Nell wanted to check on Ray. Tony's car was parked near the front entrance to The Home next to Jane's Mercury. Nell said her mother had to get Ray's adjoining apartment ready for Roberta to stay in, since Roberta was temporarily staying in Jane's apartment in the other wing, too far from her patient. Upon entering Ray's apartment, Roberta was massaging her patient's thigh while Verla held a yellow legal pad in place under Ray's right hand that clenched a pen as if he was trying to stab the paper. Roberta was gently coaxing her patient to write his name, a technique she used to stimulate the brain of patients with memory loss and determine Ray's cognitive recognition level. We all watched Ray slowly position the pen onto the paper, unable to see what he would write, if anything, as Roberta kept massaging and talking to him as if he was a little boy. Just then: we couldn't help noticing that he'd raised his tent again. Verla's sense of humor, ever present, she asked Ray, 'Is that for me?' I saw something flicker in Ray's eyes, maybe a thought as his

*hand stabbed out 4 letters that Verla read out loud to us
after Ray dropped the pen: 'not u.' We all had a good
laugh...except for Verla. To Roberta, this was a
'positive sign' that Ray was coming back."*

Trouble in a Black Dress

Tony drove us back home; the drive went fast because we were animated and excited about Ray coming out of his coma. First, I asked Tony what he was going to do with his increased share that Nell was trying to secure for their impending sale.

"I'll tell my wife I inherited some money from a distant relative. She'll put it in a safe place. She doesn't trust me with money," Tony laughed and coughed until his face turned purple.

"She's smart," Verla laughed.

Then Verla said she'd buy a new car and move out of The Argo; adding:

"Maybe buy a little house…visit Crystal in Mexico."

Tony wanted to go out to celebrate Ray's recovery since his wife is out of town. Verla suggested Al's at seven, and to pick her up here as Tony dropped us off at The Argo's back door. I wanted to walk to my place and told them I'd meet them at seven.

175

Nell was on my mind on my walk home; I was anxious to catch up on my book, then pound out some pages on Herman, knowing I had many weeks of typing ahead of me.

***

I wrote about Ray coming out of his coma, including his "not u" message for Verla before typing 10 more pages of my book. After a long shower, I got dressed and when I opened my door to go meet Tony and Verla...there was a business card that fell on the floor. It was from an *insurance company investigator, Gabe Florentine*, with a scribbled notation, *"please call me."* I figured I'd talk to Verla and Tony before I call this man about Ray's *accident.*

***

Verla and Tony were seated at a cocktail table by the dance floor. Verla was wearing her sexy black dress with the low bustline and her blonde Jayne Mansfield wig with 2" black heels. I'd only seen her wear this outfit when she was out-on-the-town with Ray; I could tell they'd already had a couple drinks by the time I joined them. Verla wore her favorite oval-shaped black onyx ring and matching earrings that Ray gave her during one of his visits. It's funny how she'd take any jewelry Ray gave her to have it appraised by Hal, one of her regulars, who had a shop a few doors down from Sammy's. It was obvious that Verla still loved Ray.

During our meal while toasting *to Ray's return*, Al came over to Verla and handed him the same business card I'd given her earlier, telling her discreetly:

"The guy in the suit at the bar, that's him."

Tony and I couldn't stop her if we wanted to; we could only watch *Jayne* get up, brush down the hem of her dress and *stomp* over to this man parked on a barstool who'd threatened her peace-of-mind ever since Ray's fall.

"Trouble in a black dress," Tony warned me as *Jayne* stood behind this man who represented all the worry and stress about Ray.

We watched her tap on the man's shoulder, and when the man turned to her, we could hear every word as if she wanted everyone to hear her:

"I'm Verla Sapp! Are you the insurance dick looking for me?"

The man looked stupefied as Verla continued:

"You tell your dicks in Des Moines that Ray Vining's going to live, and that there will be *NO* death benefit to pay. So, you and your little pencil dick can go...NOW!"

The embarrassed man could see that everyone was watching him when he said he wanted to finish his beer first. That's when Verla picked up the man's glass of beer and splashed it onto his face. We all watched the man leave the bar as Tony started the room applauding Jayne's performance. Verla bowed and helped Al clean up the mess she made before returning to our table. When T.P. tried to light a cigarette, Verla pulled the Camel out of his pooched lips and crumbled it into the ashtray, telling her sick friend:

"You don't smoke around me anymore. If you want to kill yourself...take your ass outside."

Later, when walking Verla back to her place, I told her that I looked at my mom's chakra chart this afternoon, informing my tipsy aunt that Ray is a Violet now, and that Violets are least compatible with Oranges; and, that might help explain his "not u" message to her.

She stopped on the sidewalk, looked at me intensely and laughed before saying:

"Mister Tightwad Energy...you KNOW where you can SHOVE that orange!"

Eternal Life

I spent the next week working southwest Minnesota, unloading product, writing, then typing from my notebooks on Herman every night in my motel room. I was now taking orders for my book from my repeat customers, letting them know it would cost twelve bucks a copy delivered by me when I came 'round again after I published my book. Now, every moment of every day seemed to have purpose, knowing this Friday I'd see Nell to get her feedback and a quote from her friend on my printing costs. Last Sunday, Verla said she'd meet me at The Home on Friday, since she told Sammy she wants weekends off to be with Ray. She said I could stay in her adjoining apartment and she'd make me a great meal this coming weekend.

Nothing was more obvious to me than the way I managed to stay away from old thought patterns, stopping my thoughts a thousand times a day, which gave me much more energy at night when I had to blend thinking with creativity, something my mother called *creative doing.* I discovered I didn't need as much sleep when I reduced my thoughts during the day. This allowed me to not be fearful or attached to the outcome of every prospect I called on. It truly is the only way for me to *Be* in this line of work I've chosen. Many times,

I'd roll into these little towns in *my territory,* places in the heart of tightwad energy with names like Jackson, Ruthven, and Peterson –all of them not much bigger than a few neighborhood blocks. And I'd know in these places that my father was right to have vicariously sent me here. I *feel* this every step of every day, for this is rural America, where the pace of life is slower and just right for staying out of a busy mind that wants more, more, always more. It's here where I'm meant to Be…and it's wonderful.

I wrote in my motel room in Sibley, Iowa:

"My father never reached this kind of happiness with his work after pounding away for thousands of hours on Herman. I'd fall asleep hearing the sound of Herman's keys, the sound so heavy with anger as if 'here we go again'…page after page that eventually only became paper stored in his writing crate with Herman. Lately, I hear that very same sound of the keys striking my pages while I'm walking between calls, delivering, or on my drive between these towns he sent me to. It's an addiction to write, to create something from nothing. My father never did find that one good reader as I have. Verla…I owe my chance to come up with a book to her. Changes are coming for her: Soon she'll leave Sammy's and The Argo; and, it looks like she'll lose T.P., her best friend, business partner and my mentor. After this big meeting Nell is setting up, what a shame that T.P. will have money and no time to enjoy it. Always present is this loss I can see coming to Verla, a loss tempered by her desire to keep Ray in her life."

***

Friday afternoon I arrived at the A-frame when Verla, Jane and Nell were waiting for Roberta to stop by and fill them in on something "very interesting" her patient told her during Ray's recorded speech therapy. All the women seemed to be getting along very well; and yet I could tell that Verla was anxious about what Ray recorded during his speech therapy session earlier this afternoon.

Nell was dressing casual now that she didn't have to deal with the *escort service*. Roberta arrived in her gray uniform and with a large shoulder purse that carried a cassette player she placed on the coffee table after joining us on the horseshoe sofa. We listened to Roberta and Ray on tape:

"Ray, what's the *last* thing you remember before coming out of your coma?"

There was a long pause before we heard Ray's weak voice say in his slow and deliberate cadence:

"I remember…watching…Billy's station wagon…take me to the hospital. I was covered with…Verla's purple blanket…on the roof of his car. I could see them take me off the roof…at the hospital…and put me on a gurney…"

Verla and I were gape-jaw stunned to hear this, since we never told anybody the details about getting Ray to the hospital…or ever mentioned the purple blanket. Then Ray stunned the breath right out of us when he said during the drive to the hospital he was hovering above his body and was attached to his body by a silver cord that he seemed to be keeping it attached by willing it so, adding:

181

"I just knew that if that cord pulled away…from my body…I would leave this world. I didn't want to let go."

Then Roberta asked her patient if it seemed as if he could pull this silver cord off his body if he wanted to.

"Yes!" Ray was certain.

"Ray, did you see God?"

A long pause again until:

"I can only say that…some force was keeping me…attached to that cord."

"Why didn't you want to let go of that cord, Ray?"

After a long pause:

"I was afraid…if I did…I'd go straight to hell."

Roberta clicked off her cassette player. We all stared at her with this look of stupefied awe on our faces, waiting for Ray's physical therapist to say something. Nell broke our silence when she asked Roberta if she had other patients who talked about this near-death kind of experience.

"Yes. But this one's different."

"How's that?" Verla asked for all of us.

"I believe him," Roberta stated.

Then Verla said:

"The ride to the hospital on the roof of Billy's car… My purple blanket covering him… He *couldn't* have known about any of that. Only Billy and I knew those things."

"Why was he on the roof of Billy's car?" Jane was curious.

"Because that's where he landed," I answered for Verla. "We didn't want to move him."

I had to tell them that my mother talked about people she knew who saw the same silver cord attached to them during their near-death experiences. Many people over the years came to see my mother after such an event and described it just like Ray did. I told them how one time a mother brought her young son to see my mom after he recovered from a car accident; and that the boy said things he couldn't have known about while he was unconscious.

"So, this means eternal life," Jane stated to all of us.

"What else could it mean?" Nell asked her mother.

Verla had to ask Roberta if Ray said anything else to her, anything about what happened to him.

"He asked if you were here," Roberta said to Verla.

"Can I talk to him now?" Verla asked.

"He's sleeping now. Tomorrow morning after his voice therapy would be better," Roberta said while putting her cassette player back into her purse.

"Okay," Verla nodded.

Roberta left the A-frame; she was on her way back to her temporary living space in Ray's adjoining apartment, where she planned on living until her patient recovered. We were all in a daze with this news; I got up to go outside to my van to get my notebook, wanting

183

to write this chapter in my book, this incredible plot-point in my story that was *real,* and more important than any other thing I'd written so far in my book.

Nell followed me outside to have a smoke; she asked me what I thought of all this. I told her that after I'd heard about these near-death experiences from my mom, that after a while…it wore off. I told Nell that my dad always dismissed them as *ghost stories.* I gave Nell 50 more typed pages of my book; that's when she told me she really enjoyed my writing, and that Diane said to tell you that she could give you a price near two bucks a copy for five thousand copies.

"That includes editing?"

"Everything," Nell said.

That's when I told Nell I changed all the names and locations related to Sisters of Mercy, and that I changed Ray's product line and customers of the escort service, replacing packinghouses with power plants; and, aprons, gloves and knives were changed to janitorial supplies. Nell liked that idea, and said she was going to suggest something like that. I told her I'd have 50 more typed pages for her next week, and that Diane could start editing, because I was going to publish my book.

"Good. I'll let her know."

***

Nell had set up a table and chair for me to write on the A-frame's deck. I wrote up a storm, covering Ray's recent near-death experience. Later, Verla came out to the deck and asked me if I wanted to go out for dinner, drive to the square in Denison to get a bite to eat.

"I'll buy if you drive," Verla said.

***

This time, I took my notebook with me when I drove us to town in Birdie, parking in front of a restaurant off the square, one of my good customers. We sat at a window table. I kept making notes about things Verla said about Ray and their 30-year-long relationship.

Both

After dinner, Verla and I wanted to go for a walk around the town square. Both of us wanted to get Crystal's feedback on Ray's near-death experience; and, both of us saw Ray's terrible fall into a coma as a positive life-changing event for all of us. Verla said it was more important than ever today…

"…to get that in your book, something that gives cynical people like Ray hope that there is more to life after leaving this insane world."

"My mom would sometimes invite me to sit with her in the morning on our sun porch when she meditated on stillness inside her body, putting her attention on her *God-consciousness,* she called it. When Ray's voice ended on that tape…I knew that my book was moving toward a better-feeling story…somehow. I always dismissed my mom's words about how we are all Spiritual Beings having a human experience. Mostly because my dad's addiction to negative thoughts matched the world wherever I went. And even here…until I heard Ray's voice on that tape."

Just then: Verla stopped walking. She started to cry…and she had to sit down. We found a nearby bench and I sat close to her, putting my arm around her solid shoulders as she sobbed out such grief I knew she'd been holding onto ever since Ray's fall. I didn't say anything. Like I saw my mother do so many times with her clients, I stayed open...waiting for her. I knew this had something to do with things she talked about during and after dinner, all those old memories she and Ray shared. Then, she started to talk:

"This has already changed me. Soon, I'll have the time and money to help take care of Ray...and see *if* we have anything together."

"What about the...crabs?" I had to ask, referring to Ray's past *lifestyle.*

"That's up to him. If Ray doesn't want me around...I can live any place I want..."

"Start a new life somewhere?"

"Yeah."

"Where would you go?" I asked.

"I don't know... Maybe to Mexico to visit Crystal. I want to tell her about The Home, and how it's her place to go when she's old. My adjoining apartment is hers. She may never need it...but it's there if she does."

"I know she'd love to see you. Val is a loving person. You'd like her."

"Yeah. Maybe I'll take a road trip in my new car and go see my baby sister...*after* I spend some time with Ray. Hell, maybe he'd even want to go with me... Except I'd have to watch him like a hawk around those pretty senoritas," Verla laughed her loud/wonderful laugh.

187

"Do you know the new buyer for Sisters of Mercy?" I was curious.

"No…and I don't want to know. Nell and T.P. are handling that end."

Verla got up and we continued walking around the square on the sidewalk skirting the courthouse. She said she quit smoking ever since she chased that insurance guy out of Al's, resolving to live well after Ray's awakening. I admired her positive desire for change; and she talked at length about her longtime partners Jane and Ray, and T.P., admitting she was jealous of Jane because Jane had given Ray a daughter, something she couldn't do.

"Why couldn't you?" I asked.

"I'm one of those women who didn't feel the urge to have children."

Then Verla asked me how close I was to finishing my book.

"I don't know. Since it's not really a work of art like a novel…I want to see where this Ray character goes. Are you going to tell Ray about his fall, how it happened?"

"Maybe. I'll see how he's doing tomorrow."

"That might be best."

I asked Verla if she thought Ray remembered anything that led up to his fall.

"Roberta said he doesn't know anything about it. For a long time, Ray and I were just business partners. I knew he visited girls at The Hill. I told him I didn't mix business with pleasure. But later, I broke down and broke my rule after I got out of that part of the business. He became this big test for me, to see *if* I could be loyal to one man… And I was. I want him to know it was an accident, and that I never meant for him to get hurt like he did."

"I think he must know that already."

"I hope so."

***

I spent the night in Verla's unfurnished adjoining apartment in The Home. Nell brought me a futon from Jane's apartment and I slept quite well after Verla and I stayed up late with Jane and Nell playing cards in the A-frame. Verla was going through nicotine craving on top of being anxious about talking to Ray tomorrow.

Honey and Lavender

The next mid-morning, after a big breakfast Jane made us, I drove Verla in Birdie over to The Home when Ray's vocal session was over. Verla gave me *a password: T.P.,* a signal to me that she wanted to be alone with Ray.

Upon entering Ray's room –he was standing, using a walker for the first time, his head craned forward and his white atrophied bird legs shivering while Roberta supervised his every move:

"Use your arms, Ray. Focus on *one step* at a time."

We found out later that Ray used his toilet for the first time earlier this morning before his vocal session. Ray looked up at me with his *Violet* eyes still lit with aliveness, reminding me of his recorded words yesterday.

"You remember these people, Ray?" Roberta asked before leaving the room to get her patient's lunch ready and to give us some privacy after she watched Ray move over to the window to get some sunshine on his pale body.

"You're looking good, Ray," Verla said.

Ray didn't say anything. He stood facing the morning sun, taking in the sunshine while standing inside his walker in a green hospital gown. Verla nudged my arm and said to Ray (and me):

"*T.P.* said to tell you hi, Ray."

I missed her password que because I was stunned by this transformation of this now-humble man who looked like a shy boy, so different from the man I really didn't like at all…before the fall. I left Ray's apartment after another nudge from Verla, but I stayed near the cracked-open doorway so I could eavesdrop on them without being seen as Verla moved over to the sun-bright windows to stand next to Ray. Verla talked slow and soft, yet loud enough for me to hear:

"It's good to see you on your feet, Ray"

No words from Ray. He seemed to be enjoying the warmth of sunlight on his skin. After a bit, I heard Verla ask him if he remembered *anything about that night he fell onto Billy's car?*

Still no answer; then Verla explained how she was upset with him because he gave her crabs, and that she planned to kick him in the balls, adding without any drama:

"But you fell backwards and flew out my window. Now I don't care about the crabs…or who gave them to you…but you were the *only* man I was ever loyal to. I was hurt and mad at you then, but not *now*, Ray," Verla's voice cracked and faltered with emotion.

After a long pause, Ray mumbled something.

"What, Ray?" Verla leaned closer to him to hear:

"Stripper," Ray blurted while keeping his eyes closed and facing the sunshine.

191

Afterwards, Verla told me she wanted to dump his bedside pitcher of ice water on his head, yet remained cool, smiling at his grinning face, she patted his hand on the walker and left it there until he started to move away from the window. Verla started talking, staying near him:

"I thought I'd buy some curtains today for my apartment here…"

That's when Ray turned his face to look at Verla, asking her if she was living here.

"Yes, I want to help you recover…"

Ray looked right into her eyes and said, "Honey…if you want me to recover…then *go away.*"

That's when I backed away from the door, to not see the devastated hurt on Verla's face after Ray's cool rejection of her; and that's when Roberta returned with her patient's lunch. I followed Verla outside to Birdie, whereupon she broke down. I stood there holding her as she cried for the longest time. Verla cancelled buying curtains, telling me to let Jane and Nell know she was going home and not moving into her apartment here. I didn't want her driving now.

"Ray doesn't want me here," she said without contempt, unaware that I heard everything. "I'm grateful he's alive," she kept saying, even when we went back inside The Home to her apartment where she packed her suitcase fast and I carried it out to Birdie's trunk. I hugged her and asked her if she was okay to drive. She said she was, telling me she wanted to go back to her bed and catch up on her sleep.

"What are going to do now?" I had to ask.

"I don't know, Billy. I don't have a plan B. Maybe I'll take some time off to figure out what I'm going to do. Ray's been all I've thought about ever since his fall."

"I know. You take your time and do what you want to do. Soon, you'll have money and you've got this place to fall back on when you're old."

"You too," she said.

"What do you mean?"

"You and Crystal are the beneficiaries of my apartments here."

"Really? I think I said, then watched her get a lighter and a cigarette from a pack of Winstons in Birdie's glovebox that she lit fast before giving me a ride to the bottom of the lane near the A-frame's mailbox. I told her to wait for me, because I wanted to follow her back home. She said *okay*…but when I got about half-way up the lane…she drove away. I started running for my van, but then I remembered I left my notebook in Verla's adjoining apartment where I slept last night. I had to go get it.

I decided to walk back to The Home to get my notebook, giving up on following Verla back home, since she needed space to recover from Ray's rejection of her. Nell arrived in her car at the same time I reached the front entrance; she was bringing Ray some things he wanted from his room in the A-frame: silk underwear and pajamas, along with his slippers and bathrobe.

"How'd you sleep last night on the futon?" she asked.

193

"Good," I said.

"Is Verla shopping for curtains?"

"No, she went back home. Ray told her he doesn't want her around. She told me to let you and Jane know she won't be moving in here now."

I was surprised when Nell told me she'd already read the 50 pages I'd given her yesterday. She said:

"I *really* like it. You've captured everything and changed the names to protect the guilty."

I let her know that I wanted to get back home to type all weekend, so maybe I could give her 100 pages next Friday.

"Why don't you type here? You said you have your typewriter with you. What's your typewriter's name?"

"Herman. That's what my dad named it."

"You can stay in Ray's room in the A-frame and type at his desk all night long if you want. My mom will be at her house and I'm staying at Paul's tonight."

"That sounds good," I said, knowing I didn't want to get stuck consoling Verla tonight if she was in a bad way over Ray.

Nell went into Ray's apartment to deliver his stuff while I went into Verla's adjoining apartment in the other wing of the building to get my notebook I'd left on the floor beside the futon. I paused to look around at the unfurnished apartment that Verla said my mom and I would inherit. I couldn't imagine Crystal or myself ever living here. Out in the hallway, Nell told me that Ray was going for a walk around the place and that he wanted to talk to me.

There he was: baby-stepping with his walker in his slippers and silver silk pajamas, moving toward me after exiting his room, this perfect *Violet* I'd seen the likes of a thousand times on a thousand Saturdays. There was this thin, pale boy-of-a-man who fell 30 feet and changed from being this independent macho ego –to become this interdependent Violet who needs others to remain connected to his God-source, who now is aware that he is a Spiritual Being. This was clear to me earlier when I saw my mother's chakra chart that Violet Ray would not match well with Orange Verla.

I moved alongside his walker, his pale arms flexing with each step and short roll of his *squeaking* wheels, his breathing labored a bit after such a long period of atrophy. He had this determined look of a goal in sight, and wouldn't say a word until he reached the main lobby of The Home, whereupon he stopped to catch his breath and eventually said:

"I don't want to lead Verla on. She was always damaged goods…like all four of us were."

"You mean Jane and Tony and you and Verla?"

"Yes. When I saw myself on the roof of your car…covered by that purple blanket…I told God I'd never lie again if I could stay. It got so I had to imagine being with another woman when I was with Verla. That's why I liked the room dark. No more. I don't want to use her. She's got some painful changes coming. It took this experience to wake me up. She wants a stable guy who wants just her. She deserves

195

that. And I don't have that in me for her. Even Roberta gets me aroused," Ray chuckled.

Ray started to move toward the other wing of the building when I asked him what he was going to do when he gets out of here. He stopped to look at me with those gray-green eyes lit with light and said:

"You're the first one to ask me that. Thank you for asking. After Nell closes this deal…I might head down to South America…and live there until I can't live on my own anymore. Then I can come back here to live out my final days…until the next life," he winked at me knowingly and continued moving.

Then, when we entered the other wing I asked how the four of them came together to put their money from Sisters of Mercy into this place for so many years. Again, he stopped to rest before he spoke:

"We're all throwaways, mutts from dysfunctional homes. We decided we had to take care of each other. Sisters of Mercy was our long-term health care insurance. No government handouts. This was *the good thing* Tony and Verla wanted to do right from the start. So, we all worked our day jobs, paid taxes…and provided a service for unhappy men…like me. *I* was the one who resisted this place…and now *I'm* the first one to live here," he chuckled a bit at the irony.

By the time we returned to Ray's room –he was exhausted. I helped him get onto his bed, and before I left his room he told me to keep an eye on Verla, adding:

"She goes down hard when she's hurt. She'll burn her lavender candles, play her sad songs, put on her wig...and watch out...*here comes Verla.*"

***

At Ray's desk in his A-frame bedroom, I typed from 7 P.M. until 3 in the morning, pounding Herman's keys at my dad's pace, cranking out a page every half-hour. And like D. D. Wadstone, I'd finish a page then step out onto the deck to have a smoke, stretching my eyes from the page into these scenic hills my father sent me to. I'd find myself pacing back and forth across the deck, thinking about Verla and what Ray said earlier.

When I got up late the next morning, I had 15 more pages to give Nell when she and her mother stopped by to make breakfast just when I'd finished writing a letter to Verla that I wanted to put in my book in this chapter:

"Facing these hills in the morning sunlight, I can almost smell your lavender-scented candles burning and see your unmade Murphy bed minus the purple blanket I imagined you'd stuffed down your garbage chute last night. I wanted to tell you that I too had thrown away a bad habit...and found a new life for myself because of you and your belief in me to create something good with my writing. Ray has helped me see that my mother was right about all of us being Spiritual Beings, most of us unaware of this -until some miracle in a most-unlikely form like Ray Vining reminds us. Ray doesn't love you the way you want him to...because he's new, and on a new path, perhaps to South America, he told me. I trust you will move on and do good things for yourself. I love you, Billy."

The Rescue

B
y the time I returned to Woodbury late Sunday afternoon I had a *feeling* I should check on Verla before going home to type some more pages in my apartment. Ray's rejection most likely had sent her into one of her depressions involving alcohol, a wig, 2" inch heels, makeup, and a regrettable one-night stand with God knows who. *"That's my pattern,"* she laughed, *"and my generation's way of handling stuff."* I understood what she was saying. I watched my dad use the same excuse with his legal liquid pain killer that's ruined more lives than all illegal drugs combined. Many times, I would hear my mom ask my dad why he would poison his body with a depressant when he's sad, angry, and depressed about his life. My mom and I wished just once he would've answered truthfully by admitting he's sick and addicted and needs help. His ego wouldn't surrender. No way was I going to let Verla go down that path.

I parked my van next to Birdie in my old parking space when old Klem was coming out the back door with his girlfriend from The Hill, Marie or Maria, I'm not sure of her name. She held onto his arm; they looked tipsy and happy as they fell into a cab laughing. I found out earlier from Verla that Klem was living below his means in The Argo because he was paying for his sister's assisted-living care in a top-of-the-line facility that cost him four grand a month. *"A guy like that deserves to have some fun,"* Verla told me.

Verla didn't answer my *loud knocking* on her door, so I used my key, and right away my senses picked up what Ray and I knew about her: The heavy odors of cigarette smoke and Scotch breath; the ashtrays overflowing with Winston butts and another brand that told me she had a visitor last night; her bed was down, the pink satin sheets twisted and wrinkled with no purple blanket in sight. I opened her cracked-open windows all the way to let in fresh cold air from a Canadian cold front that had just begun blasting wind and freezing sleet over the concrete ledge outside her window. I emptied the ashtrays into an empty carry-out pizza box and dropped it down the garbage chute out in the hallway. I picked up her clothes on the floor and tossed them onto her full closet laundry basket along with her pink satin sheets before putting on another bottom sheet and lifting and standing her Murphy bed into the storage closet. The whole time I was cleaning her apartment –I was unconscious about how I kept seeing my mother doing the same chores for my father when she'd go over to his apartment to check on him every now and then when he was missing in action, and not returning her calls.

I checked Tommy's empty bar downstairs that was closed on Sundays before I peered into the near-empty dumpster in the basement, curious if her purple blanket was in there. I figured it was in the city dump by now after last night's pick-up. I decided not to leave a note on Birdie's windshield before driving over to the bowling alley, since sometimes she'd have a drink with

Al on Sundays, just the two of them. Again: she wasn't there.

***

I pounded out another 15 pages on Herman in my apartment until 2 A.M., falling fast into sleep on my warm and cozy bed while an ice storm covered Woodbury with freezing whiteness and howling winds.

***

Around 3:30 A.M., *blaring SIRENS* from firetrucks awoke me from a deep sleep. It *sounded* close when the sirens…stopped. My mind gave me a terrifying thought, causing me to bolt-up in bed, after recalling the cigarette butts I'd hastily dumped down Verla's garbage chute. I dressed faster than I ever had at this hour, finding myself running and slipping several times on the frozen sidewalks. From a block away, I could see 3 firetrucks surrounding The Argo as shivering residents in nightwear huddled together in front of the hotel like displaced penguins. I ran to the back of the hotel where I could see black smoke pouring out from Verla's open window as naked Verla stood outside on the frozen ledge, her head turned away from the smoke with her arms crossed over her bare breasts.

Later, I found out she had passed out drunk and naked on her bed until she woke up coughing from smoke pouring through her open dormer. She'd opened her apartment door and had to close it again since the hallway was filled with smoke with smoke detector *alarms* going off in her apartment and several on the 3rd floor.

Now: a spotlight from the firetruck lit up Verla's naked body, revealing that she was still wearing her Donna Reed wig as the firetruck's ladder moved into position with a brave fireman on the ascending platform closing-in-on a dramatic rescue. The spotlight afforded a TV crew and local newspaper photographer good lighting to capture this dramatic scene while frantic Tommy was confirming to firemen that all residents were accounted for…except for Klem. That's when I let Tommy know that I'd seen Klem getting into a cab and leaving with his girlfriend earlier.

There it was: I saw the instant the photo was taken that would be front-page news tomorrow, just when the heroic fireman had helped Verla onto his hydraulic ladder platform, he covered her upper body with a blanket and her bare butt was lit up and facing the cameras. As the ladder descended I knew that at least Verla's depression over Ray was over.

Fireman Dan

Sammy opened up his café as a safe holding space for his brother's displaced tenants, serving them all hot coffee and breakfast while they waited for the fire department to allow them back into the building. I had run back to get my van to shuttle Verla and 3 loads of residents to Sammy's since firetrucks blocked most of the vehicles of residents. After my last run, there was Verla, seated in the same booth when I first arrived on the bus from L.A. She sat on the edge of the booth with the fire department blanket over her shoulders and wearing a cook's uniform she'd put on in Sammy's office. She was soaking her feet in a large pan of *warm* water, something Fireman Dan told her to do after he got her a pair of wool socks that he put on her feet right after he got her down to safety. I wanted to remember every detail of this scene for my book, since this was a perfect example of the local characters my dad had written about in his notebooks I'd found in his crate. Later, I wrote:

"Sammy's was alive with noisy chatter from the hotel evacuees until Tommy, who was busy serving them hot coffee and food his brother was making in the kitchen, stood on a chair, yelling for 'QUIET, PLEASE!!' until the noise stopped. Then he said, 'The fire department

will stop by here and let us know when it's safe to go back!'

Earlier, firemen had to axe their way into Klem's totaled apartment to put out the source of the fire started by a cigarette butt in the bathroom trash can that caught a roll of toilet paper on fire that spread to cheap particle board cabinets. Smoke poured from Klem's open dormer into the hallway and Verla's apartment via her open dormer. Verla and I let Tommy know that this was the night Klem stayed with Maria, his ex-Sister of Mercy from The Hill, who now had an apartment that old Klem was paying for.

Verla told me that she asked her rescuer his name when he was putting socks on her feet and massaging them. 'Dan,' he smiled at her; and Verla was in love. She said she hugged this middle-aged man who saved her life, offering him a free breakfast anytime in Sammy's. 'I might just take you up on that,' Fireman Dan smiled at this woman's face that was smeared with lipstick, mascara, blue eye shadow and a smoky wig that reminded him of some actress he'd seen on TV. From that moment on, Verla said she met the man she would spend the rest of her life with. I was so grateful she was alive and happy."

***

"How long were you out there on that ledge?" Sammy asked his soon-to-be-retired day manager.

"Long enough to know I'm in love," she fluttered her eyes when Sammy handed her a towel and took away the bucket while Verla put on those wool socks Fireman Dan gave her. "I told him breakfast on me...anytime."

"You won't be here; you're retiring," her boss teased.

"I know what you're trying to do here, Sammy Argo.... Just get me a cup of coffee," she fake-pounded the top of the table and *laughed* her big loud Verla way that made Sammy laugh and got everyone's attention.

I sat next to her in the booth, knowing that Verla Sapp is everything that tightwad energy is not. Her presence made me realize that this is how people should relate to each other: open and real. Here, were some three dozen displaced Argo residents in their nightwear, laughing and enjoying the moment while the Argo brothers served them coffee and breakfast two hours before the café opened for business. The recent stress of their evacuation was overcome by the warmth and brotherly love felt by all of us in this family business that was sorely going to miss my aunt when she retired. I wrote later:

"I saw these solitary Argo tenants transformed from tightwad energy to this united group of people concerned about each other. The energy in Sammy's was electric; it was like one big family...that got along. Then, a funny thing happened around 6 A.M. when the café opened every morning: a cab double-parked in front and Klem and his 'snuggle bunny' Maria got out. The buzzing café turned to dead silence, for all of them had heard Klem was the cause of their long night. Verla knew that her neighbor probably knew nothing about the fire, having spent the night in Maria's apartment. Verla was at her best when Klem and Maria sat across from us at our table oblivious to the early crowd staring at them. Verla leaned over our table and yelled in the direction of Klem's good ear: 'I got good news and bad news, Klem!

The good news is you don't live in The Argo!' Klem was confused as Verla continued: 'The bad news is...Tommy's on his way to our table!'

I left the booth with Verla, not wanting to hear Tommy tell-off the careless old man who nearly burned down his hotel. Just then: a firetruck with flashers on double-parked in front of Sammy's. We saw Fireman Dan get out from behind the wheel, his bald head soon shining into Verla's loving eyes as she quickly neat-folded the blanket 'Mr. Perfect' gave her. Being the son of a passionate writer –I felt my storyline moving in the direction of a happy ending for Verla. From my vantage point I could see the instant Verla saw her hero enter the café –that he liked her too. I kept watching them in the din of background noise of Tommy yelling into Klem's hearing aid, 'I don't give a shit where you live! All I know is it won't be in The Argo! And no way in hell are you getting your deposit back! Your apartment is trashed! Your TV is melted and so is your electric razor and all your clothes!'

I'd never seen Verla make a fresh pot of coffee so fast as she did while Fireman Dan let Tommy know his tenants could go back home now. Then, the middle-aged hero sat on T.P.'s stool at the counter, chatting with the blushing woman in the smoky Donna Reed wig he'd rescued just a couple hours ago. She re-filled his carry-out coffee and watched him drive away in the firetruck before twirling around like a high school cheerleader and walking over to me, she said, 'He's coming by for his free breakfast at noon when his shift is over.' Then, she gushed her words in my face, 'Billy, this is the man I've been waiting for. I can feel it, Billy. I need a ride home to shower and change into my uniform.' Then,

Verla addressed the room: 'Anybody wanting a ride home, get in line behind me! Let's go!'

I dropped 'Donna' off at the hotel's back door with a full load of passengers who were happy to return home after a long night without much suffering, thanks to the waitress whose bottom would be 'blurred out' and headlined in this morning's paper and lead story on all 3 Woodbury TV stations."

***

This was a period when Verla and "Danny" started dating right after that *free breakfast* Verla served her hero, the man she somehow knew she'd spend the rest of her life with, *"even if we're both in The Home,"* she laughed. Dan Gordon was a lifelong bachelor who told his new girlfriend he was retiring in just 3 weeks after 30 years with the fire department. Danny had fallen head-over-heels for his first steady girlfriend in 14 years. A few days ago, after I'd mailed another 50 pages of my book straight to Diane in Omaha for editing, Verla stopped by my apartment to let me know she was retired from Sammy's and that she and Danny were shopping for a used RV to travel all over the country.

"We agreed to split all expenses, even the cost of the RV. And Danny loves to eat. I can cook for him and he said I could park Birdie in his garage until he sells his house. He's open to living in Ensenada, Billy. And he wants me to move out of that firetrap and move in with him until we hit the road together. I gave Tommy notice the other day."

"You think you'll get married?"

"No way. We both don't want that right now. I told him I had some property to sell in Omaha first. I'm not telling him anything about Sisters of Mercy or my past life at The Hill."

"That's smart. The dead past is not who you are now."

"That's right. And…I quit smoking and drinking. Ever since our first date. He doesn't drink or smoke."

"I'm happy for you, Verla."

***

I'd never seen such a transformation in someone; Verla changed her eating habits and gave away all her wigs and most of her wardrobe. I was invited over for dinner at Danny's house and Verla made the best meal I think I've ever had. I left that house knowing my favorite aunt was healthier and happier than she'd ever been in her life. Verla's story was headed for a happy ending; and yet I knew there was something missing in the storyteller.

When Verla Left

Within two months, Verla and Danny were driving to Mexico to visit Crystal and Val in their '73 Winnebago with low mileage they'd bought from a retired fireman with health issues. Going-away parties at Al's and Sammy's were packed. The happy couple planned to be on the road for a year, seeing the whole country.

***

For the last couple months, I worked my route until my printer, Diane, was close to having my book ready for my final proof reading. Nell had become a caregiver for both Ray and Jane. Jane had a bad fall and was bedridden in her house; she had fractures in her back and a broken ankle, forcing Nell to confront her mother about selling her house in Denison and moving into The Home with Ray, so Roberta could care for both of them. Jane resisted that idea. Ray was getting around with a cane, and sneaking out of The Home, getting a ride from a Denison buddy to a watering hole they liked. Nell told me on the phone that *"Ray's acting like a spoiled brat, wanting me to take him everywhere, refusing to do his therapy if I don't chauffeur him around."*

I told Nell that ever since Verla left, most of the excitement about having my book published was all but gone. When I got off the phone with Nell, I realized that the life I knew here –went away with Verla. I drove downtown to Sammy's to have breakfast the other day and heard from Sammy that old Klem moved to Omaha into an assisted-living home to be near his daughter and grandkids. Tony was there, dunking his burnt toast in his coffee while reading his paper. Instead of his worn sales case at his feet, there was his portable oxygen tank with plastic tubes inserted in his nostrils. And he was still smoking, because I could see a butted Camel non-filter in his ashtray; this was more proof that Verla was gone, since she enforced a no-smoking rule in Sammy's for her old friend.

As I sat there next to Tony at Sammy's counter, I looked around the café that was noticeably quiet compared to when Verla was here. Then Tony lamented about his wife wanting him to move into The Home since he was having too much pain and she was unable to do much at home with her arthritis. I wrote later, the next Monday in a Fort Dodge motel room:

"When Verla left, it's like the center of my universe was gone, and my story turned into this dull period of working my route half-heartedly, telling my customers with markedly-less enthusiasm that my book would be ready soon. Missing her had affected my sales and the thrill of my first book coming out. Then: when I called on my big packinghouse accounts in Mason City then Fort Dodge - two big customers for Ray and Sisters of Mercy - I found out that both purchasing agents and 36 total executives had been fired without notice. The new purchasing agents had no clue why the massive

'housecleaning.' This news had my ears ringing with confusing possibilities related to Sisters of Mercy."

***

This massive firing news changed my route from heading east to Waterloo to working my way south to Carroll, another plant on Ray's route. If I heard the same news in Carroll, I'd go to Denison to inform Nell, since this might affect the *big sale* she was about to close. And, concerning my book, this might be the perfect timing my dad always hoped for whenever he submitted one of his stories.

***

By early Tuesday afternoon, I was on my way to Denison upon hearing the same news that 16 executives in the Carroll *power plant* were fired for undisclosed reasons. Perhaps the corporate headquarters in Chicago found out about the bogus invoices for aprons, gloves and knives that paid for Sisters of Mercy visits.

I drove to the A-frame, confident that Nell had to know about this, since her step-dad worked at the Denison *power plant* and he might've been canned too. My busy mind took over my body, thinking over the possibilities of The Family losing their chance to sell the service that would sustain the future of The Home. I parked at the bottom of the muddy lane right when the mail truck drove away. No vehicles and nobody home at the A-frame. No way was I going to take that muddy trail that led down to The Home. I was tired and angry with myself for letting this news about those fired executives run my mind with non-stop chatter that was

210

all about the fear of The Family losing their big sale and how that would affect my book sales.

If I hadn't seen that mail truck earlier, I would have never even looked inside that mailbox and found a letter postmarked in Mexico from *Verla Gordon* addressed to *Ray Vining.* I wanted to tear it open now…before I drove over to The Home. My mind kept telling me that if I didn't open it now before delivering it to Ray –I might never find out something I *should* know. But then: I couldn't just open a personal letter. Soon, as I approached The Home –something was different: There were no vehicles parked near the front entrance as usual, even Roberta's dark blue Rambler wasn't there. I remember Nell telling me on the phone a couple weeks ago that Roberta was taking Ray with her to Denison whenever Roberta gave Jane her rehab. sessions in Jane's house after Jane's fall.

After checking all the locked doors at The Home, I drove over to Jane's house that I'd driven past once when Verla showed me where she lived. Again: no vehicles at Jane's house, and nobody answered the door. The garage door was down, so I didn't know if Jane's car was there. My next option: the Denison plant, where Jane's ex-husband and Nell's step-dad, Bob Jasper, is the plant manager and one of Ray's first *clients. What if Jasper was fired like the rest of them?*

A friendly receptionist at the Denison plant told me that Mr. Jasper took an *early retirement*, along with a bunch of other executives. All she knew was that he lived in Harlan, not far from Denison.

***

Within 30 minutes I was in a Harlan DQ grabbing a bite to eat and found *Robert Jasper*'s address listed in the phone book. I found myself wishing I'd tried to find Roberta first, instead of a recent *early retiree* who might not want to see anybody at this juncture. When I parked in front of 301 Cedar Street, I saw a *For Sale* sign planted in front of Bob Jasper's house. This whole scene was familiar to me now, reminding me of one of my dad's Twilight Zone episodes I'd found in his crate, "Silent Witness." As I walked toward the front door I recalled my dad's scene where the lead character, a blind man, who was searching for this man who had witnessed the hit-and-run car accident that killed his seeing-eye dog. Turns out, the witness was *deaf and dumb* and feared getting involved because the man driving the car was his brother.

The Jasper house was empty. I drove back to the A-frame. Nobody home. This time I walked around to the deck and could see through the curtain slit behind the locked sliding glass door that the horseshoe sofa was covered with sheets as if nobody lived there now. Back to The Home I drove; same story: no vehicles and Ray's apartment windows were curtained shut. I needed a cigarette. I quit smoking when Verla finally did, the same day she served Fireman Dan his free breakfast at Sammy's. I decided to drive back into Denison to the bar where Jane and Ray used to hang out. Maybe I could get some smokes there and find out where Paul's farm is, Nell's boyfriend. Bartenders know everybody in a small town. But then: after starting my van in front of The Home, I remembered the letter from Verla addressed to Ray I'd put in my jacket pocket. It was

time to turn on my dome light and read it. This Paul
Drake investigative was draining my energy.

Until the Heat Cools

"**D**ear Ray, I thought it was time to let you all know that I married Fireman Dan in Vegas, the man who rescued me from the ledge of my apartment. Right before we went inside the chapel in Vegas...I stopped on my cold feet and told him it's my turn to rescue him, that we can turn around now and head down to Mexico, and I really won't mind. He looked right into my eyes and said let's jump. I must say that the waterworks started and now I'm Mrs. Gordon. I'll bet you never thought in your wildest dreams that I'd get hitched. I had to write to you, Ray, to tell you I was thinking about you when I was bare-ass naked on that freezing ledge. I thought about you, and what you said about not wanting to let go of this life. I felt the same way, that I too could be jumping into hell. That's why I didn't jump. But then, I lost that fear, because of what you saw when Billy and I drove you to the hospital. And then: I heard the sirens of the firetrucks...and there was this man...a man who I didn't know, who was coming up to the same window and bringing new light into my life just as it happened for you. It's all so strange and wonderful, Ray, how both of us are getting this second chance to live a better life. I do think it's a good plan for all of you to stay in The Hill until the heat cools. I* *must go now; I certainly owe Billy a letter. Love always, Verla"*

***

By the time I arrived in Woodbury it was getting late. I drove by The Hill and could see all the familiar vehicles of The Family, all parked near the back-door entrance. *Until the heat cools,* was something I'd deal with tomorrow, because I didn't want to ask Nort or his wife to unlock the back door for me and be tempted to buy a pack of cigarettes I really didn't want.

My letter from Verla was waiting for me in my mailbox. I hurried upstairs to open it.

"Dear Billy, I've never been happier in my life. Yes, we got hitched in Vegas. Danny and I are staying for an extended honeymoon with your mother and Val. It's so good to be with them. They are so happy together. We both had our 'readings' from Crystal soon after arriving. Danny's a Blue. Crystal says it's my perfect match. I didn't need her chakra reading to tell me that. By now you must know that Sisters of Mercy was sold, and for 8 million bucks. This is such good news for The Family: T.P. and me, Ray, Jane and Nell, you and Crystal, we each get 1 million. The other million goes to 20 of the 'sisters'; that's 50K each –as long as each one agrees to get out of the escort service business for good. 10% of each family member's share goes into a trust fund that Nell has set up for the long-term care expenses for each of us. Combined with what's already in that fund –we should be covered when we need The Home in our golden years. Because of your writing, Billy, Nell was able to sell "T.E." to the board of directors of the Chicago-based corporation that owns all the locations

215

*involved. I had copied your early notebooks for Diane
to edit and used your original story for impact. There
were 2 copies printed by Diane in Omaha. One for the
board and one for you. I gave your spare apartment key
to T.P. with instructions to put your copy inside your
dad's crate after the sale was final and when you were
out of town and on your route.*

*I'm sure you can realize that this is the one good
reader your dad always wanted for his stories. Your dad
wrote the last chapter of your book that I inserted. After
you read it –I know you'll understand. David wrote
"Crystal's Light" before they left for California; and
your mother sent it to me long before she sent you to live
with me. Yes, you were the key to this long-term project.
And, for this project to have worked as it did –you'll
come to know that you had to be the last one to know
about it. "T.E." is the story that Crystal and I wanted
you to write...for you, your father, and The Family.
Crystal and I wanted to do something like this together,
way back when we went our separate ways. Crystal
went in search of the light of God...while I stayed in
darkness. We were the original Sisters of Mercy.*

*All of us have no doubt that it was your writing that
made this project work. Billy, when I first read your
work in Sammy's, I knew you could do what your father
failed to do. Your mother offered the project to your
father...and he dismissed it...because his ego told him it
wasn't his story. I just hope you're not too upset with us
for using your talent to complete this project. Don't feel
sorry for the buyer: Nell researched the most recent
quarterly profits and 8 million is one day's profit for
them. You at least have enough money to write your
next book –if that's what you want to do. Or, you can*

216

keep your business going, and tell your customers that you're going to keep working on your book until it's ready, getting more and more customers along the way.

Yes, thanks to you, The Family was able to get out of that dark business we used as a means to an end for so many years. Most people live this way, I've discovered. See Nell in The Hill. She's waiting to give you your share – minus the 10% for your share in The Home's trust fund to cover long-term expenses for each of us...when needed. Please call me after you've read your dad's last chapter. Love always, Verla."

Unconsciously, I folded Verla's letter back into the envelope and put it on the kitchen counter next to Ray's letter. My mind kept swimming in Verla's words, splashing back and forth over all this money. And my mom's *project* with Verla that began even before I was born, that included inserting my dad's writing at the end of my book. Then, flooding to the top were all those faces of my customers – thousands of them – who were waiting to buy *my book,* only because I had earned their business with a dream product *I had created? Or was I led by these characters in my book to follow their blueprint for their story that they planned...long before I arrived?* I always had this *feeling* that my success since moving to Woodbury fell into place with help from somewhere and without the struggle I'd seen my dad go through. Then, I realized that Verla was smart to have paid me for my writing, so in some way she could claim her right to sell it.

Before I could open the lid of that green and yellow crate –I did what Crystal taught me to do: I observed my emotions rising to my head, now flush with a fire that I *knew* was anger from being manipulated from the day I boarded that bus in downtown L.A. Then: back to the money –more money than I could ever get from selling ten books in a decade to my customers. Standing over the crate, I was unable to stop my mind from showing me my characters: Verla and T.P., Ray and Jane and Nell…all of them playing a role for me…to get that *big sale* they'd all been waiting for.

I raised the lid of the crate that Tony had found when I was gone. There was Donna's fresh face, smiling down at Verla's folded purple blanket, the same one that had covered Ray's body on that awful drive to the hospital. I removed the blanket from the crate and felt the weight of *something* wrapped inside it, placing it carefully on the counter beside Verla's letters. Inside the blanket was my first book, "Tightwad Energy"; it was the only other copy printed by Diane, a trade-sized paperback with the same covers I had her design, except, at the bottom was printed: "A Novel by D. D. Wadstone." Inside the book was a return envelope from The Library of Congress. It was a copyright form confirming that "Tightwad Energy" was authored by D. D. Wadstone. Riffing through the book I saw that they were all my chapters I'd written – the original version – that Verla said she copied, except: the last chapter, "Crystal's Light," that Verla said my dad had written before he and Crystal ran off together to California.

Next: the last item wrapped in the blanket, a 9"x12", 3-pronged manuscript folder, the same kind my dad used as covers for his scripts. I opened the cover to the title page: "Crystal's Light" / a story by / D. D. Wadstone / centered on 3 lines. I cross-referenced the text from the first page of the paperback's last chapter with his original manuscript and they were a match word-for-word, except Diane must have edited it to fit my writing style. I wanted to read the edited version the way it read in my copy, so I took it to my bed, and began reading the last chapter of "T.E." under my bedside lamp.

Crystal's Light

"A story is just a story…until it points to God within."

-Crystal Sapp

"My name is David Wadstone. In the early 1950s, after only one blind date with Crystal Sapp –I fell head-over-heels in love. Crystal's big sister, Verla, arranged our date. Verla was a colorful character, a waitress in Sammy's Café in downtown Woodbury. I worked as a delivery man for a wholesale company out of Omaha. Sammy's was on my weekly route; that's how I came to know Verla. She'd buy me a cup of coffee and we'd talk about everything under the sun, including my dream to become a published writer.

I found myself arranging my breakfast or lunch break in Sammy's –just because I liked Verla's company. I'd tell her about my stories I'd written and how I was saving my money to move out to New York or Hollywood where most writers live and get discovered. Verla was the first person to show any interest in my writing. I'd talk about my stories, how dark and dirty they were, with usually a dry sense of irony found in the *ending. She wanted to read one of my stories, so I described the storylines of a half-dozen or so that I planned on taking with me as my calling cards when I leave this part of the country that Crystal and I call the land of tightwad energy. Verla picked my short story, "Sister of Mercy," after I'd given her this synopsis:*

It's about a young man from Scottsbluff, Nebraska, who gets stranded in Omaha during a winter blizzard after the war in 1946. During a white-out he stumbles into a small hotel called The Hill in downtown Omaha that turns out to be a brothel for farmers and ranchers who deliver and sell their livestock to the nearby stockyards. The hotel's ten rooms were always occupied by ten 'ladies of the night.' The hotel's discreet owner would only show his regular customers risqué photos of these women who lived in the hotel. If you weren't a regular: "No vacancy" was the owner's firm response. During this one particularly slow night with freezing temperatures, the owner didn't want to turn this polite young man out into the freezing-cold Omaha night. The owner informed the young man about his 'female occupants' who charge a hundred bucks a night, and that since it was a slow night, he'd let the young man pick a 'roommate' for the night from his photo album.

Long story, short, the young man parted with all the money he had or face freezing to death on the frozen brick streets of Omaha and picked 'Sheila' from the man's revealing photo album.

Next day, after the storm blew over, the hotel's maid found Sheila had been strangled to death and the young man's dead body hanging from a chandelier.

221

Verla liked that storyline, especially after she read the whole manuscript the next week when it revealed that Sheila's visitor was her insane brother, who had been sent to Omaha by their strict parents to return home with his sister...dead or alive.

***

Not long after reading "Sister of Mercy," Verla set me up on a blind date with her kid sister, Crystal. This girl from Council Bluffs held my attention from the first instant I laid eyes on her in Sammy's, the night of our first date, a double-date with Verla and her friend Ray from Omaha, who Verla said was a business associate.

Crystal had the opposite personality of her brash and loud sister; these were two sisters who couldn't have been more different. Crystal had light emanating from her blue-green eyes, a light I'd never seen before. We hit it off right away; and Verla knew that we would. We all went to a dance with Tommy Dorsey playing in the Martin Ballroom in downtown Woodbury. Crystal was fresh out of high school and had never dated anybody. Verla let Crystal have a few sips of her gin and tonic to loosen her sister up. After a fun night of dancing I believe the gin was the only reason Crystal let me sneak into her boardinghouse bedroom window after 2 in the morning. Verla was paying her sister's rent until she could get on her feet.

Next late morning, the four of us had a late breakfast at Sammy's. Verla the matchmaker was thrilled when she saw Crystal and me holding hands and obviously in-love 'the morning after.' That's when Ray was interested in finding out more about my story, "Sister of Mercy," that Verla must've told him about. I didn't really want to talk about it now while Crystal held my hand. But Ray kept saying how interesting it was to have photos of the women living in that hotel and wanted to know where I got that idea from. Ray wanted to know other details about the brothel that I really didn't know. That's when Crystal started talking about the unconscious male ego, and how women have given away their power to men for their own temporary security. It made such an impression on me when she lectured me about how my story was a typical example of what she called the ego's unconsciousness that causes all human violence and suffering. I could tell that Verla had heard this before, while Ray was a blank stare without a clue. I found Crystal's words fascinating. Here was this incredible young woman who had really captured the essence of one of my stories that I was unable to articulate. Every word she spoke I wanted to write down, so I could use her words in my summary of "Sister of Mercy" when I submit it to agents in New York and Hollywood.

***

Soon, Crystal was working as a waitress in Sammy's while I was driving back and forth from Omaha to Woodbury 3 or 4 times a week to be with my enlightened girlfriend I couldn't get enough of. During one of my visits, Crystal informed me that Verla was working as a prostitute for Ray in this small hotel Ray bought and recently named The Hill, the same name I'd used in my fictional story that Verla read. I was stunned by this bizarre brothel revelation until Crystal explained Verla's story, how young Verla was sexually abused by their biological father up until their parents were killed in a car accident near Missouri Valley.

Crystal told me how protective Verla was of her, making sure they were not separated in different foster homes while ever so vigilant about her baby sister's care. "She was more like my mother," Crystal said. When Crystal was 3 months pregnant, Verla was our best man at our courthouse wedding in Elk Point. A couple months later, Verla gave us the extra money we needed to move to California to start a new life far away from her sister's dark life as a call girl. I'm not sure if it was morning sickness or Verla's life at The Hill with this low-life Ray character, but Crystal cried most of the way to California. Something inside me told me it was my "Sister of Mercy" story that Crystal believed had played a part in Verla's increasing interest in her line of work.

Crystal believes that ego unconsciousness is the root cause of all evil and negatives. It's something I'd heard about...and agreed with her about...even though I resented hearing about how unconscious I am. The morning we left the land of tightwad energy for California, I noticed that Crystal's light had dimmed whenever I looked at her. I wanted to believe that it was morning sickness - that our first child was causing it - instead of the stories of mine she'd read. Already I can see that we got hitched because we had to. I wanted to believe she could help me sell my stories in Hollywood. I knew that Crystal was right about "Sister of Mercy," that it is a dark story that Verla and Ray only liked because they could use it to exploit and prosper from this same male unconsciousness that Crystal sees in me."

From Now On

How strange to wake up rich…and still be asleep; and even stranger to walk into Sammy's for breakfast –and *nobody was there.* I was that nobody. At first, I dismissed my new *self* because after my breakfast and after a writing session –I would have more money than I ever imagined…and from *my writing.* For me, this *story* hadn't ended just because of the big sale. I liked the idea that I had no clue about what I would do next, so I started to write about my life-changing dreams I had last night after reading "Crystal's Light."

"I sat at Verla's table, where we always sat together on our smoke break. The 'empty' ashtray reminded me how I was able to leave my mind last night, going right to sleep without the usual mind talk about future and past. Two vivid dreams came to me. The first one was a way of shocking me awake, which I believed began to happen when I read Verla's letters. In this dream, I know I was 'the watcher,' a thing my mother always said I was, yet never really believed her. I can't recall ever having such a dream in such vivid metallic colors: of a man's body lying on the ground at night after being electrocuted by a downed power line after a storm. For an instant –I thought it was my dead body until I saw

225

this alien-like robot examining this body, going inside the body. As the dreamer it became clear that I was watching me watching this scene from above –just as Ray had watched his body on the ride to the hospital. And then, this 2nd dream came right after that: Again, the point of view was from above as the watcher from the skylight of my high school gym in Culver City, the same silhouette of a body went through the gym hardwood floor just as Ray's body imprint was left behind on the roof of my station wagon when he was taken away into the hospital. This fountain of misty silver blood sizzled up from this body imprint on the gym floor. Even when dreaming –I was aware that I was dreaming and that both bodies were mine. Upon waking this morning, I told myself that I will pay attention to my thoughts and stop them. They are not me. I will go with a spontaneous aliveness that Crystal always had and my father resisted his entire life. I resisted it too –for him. And I refuse to resist what The Family has done with my story. I accept it and will live in my own truth, just as I know that robot in my dream was shocking my heart to awaken me. When I was showering I realized that my 2nd dream about my body imprint on the school gym's hardwood was about my junior year when I tried out for the varsity basketball team and didn't make the team. It really hit my self-image hard after being cut while my friends made the team. That's when I started smoking weed with my Grateful Dead friends. I had allowed that rejection to shape my identity in high school. I'd go to the home games stoned and actually hoped my school would lose. Talk about an unconscious ego."

***

I drove my van to the parking area behind The Hill and parked next to Jane's black Mercury. I knew the back door would be locked…but I checked it anyway and it was. I could feel Nort's wife watching me from her upstairs apartment window like some dark cloud hovering, reminding me of my dreams last night. Through Nort's back door I went…with not *one thought* coming to mind. Nort was there, in a way, standing at his register, his furtive leer on me when the tingling bell above his back door sounded the alarm that someone was here.

From now on, came between my ears, a friendly reminder, *that I don't mind anything.*

"Hey, Nort! Can you unlock the back door for me?" I pointed. "They're expecting me."

Nort grabbed his key near the register; I followed him outside to The Hill back door, still, not a thought about anything between my ears. After opening and holding the door open for me, I said, "Thanks, Nort." And something strange happened: Nort smiled at me, and he said with a humble politeness, "You're welcome."

Climbing those two flights of unbroken stairs, I was not at all anxious about who I'd find here when I pressed the worn door *buzzer* I could hear on the other side of the metal door with the one-way window. Soon, I felt some presence looking at me and Nell's smiling face was there, letting me in and saying, "I just tried to call you."

There was no feeling of anger in me or self-doubt; I was aware that my old pattern would have been to blame her for being part of this manipulation for the *big sale.* I really felt gratitude for the whole thing when I told her that Verla said I should come by to pick up my share from you. I followed her to a parlor, a room Verla had furnished for waiting *customers* soon after she and Ray started Sisters of Mercy. The Family was all there - except for Verla -; they all seemed to be watching for my mood after the big sale. Tony was seated by the open window smoking with his oxygen tank; he smiled at me, exhaling from his nostrils and said, "Good job, Billy." Jane was seated on a sofa next to Ray; she had a walker parked beside her and smiling big as Ray was looking at me with his new eyes, seeming to know I was not the same Billy-mind. I sat down on an old armchair near Tony when smiling Nell handed me a check for 900K, adding, "Ten percent of your share went into The Home trust fund."

"I know. Verla told me."

That's when I took Verla's letter from my jacket pocket and gave it to Ray, explaining that I opened it yesterday when I went to the A-frame and the mail came when I was there… Ray waved it off as if it was no big deal and read his letter, laughing at the same words I didn't find so humorous yesterday when I'd read that my book had been used for this big sale.

"You have any questions, Billy?" Tony asked.

I could see that they were all listening for my response. I wasn't thinking of a question now. Nothing I could ask, mattered, so I shook my head '*no*' right when Jane started to read Verla's letter to Ray…and she too was enjoying it. Then Nell leaned over to me and asked me from her chair:

"Billy, are you okay with this?"

"I don't mind…really…*everybody…I don't mind.*"

Ray cackled at my response, slapping his thigh and convulsing as if he knew what I had discovered. Then, a question did come to mind:

"Ray, did my dad's story, "Sister of Mercy," give you and Verla the idea to get your service going the way you did?"

"It *sure* did," Ray admitted.

"Did my dad ever know that?"

"I don't know," Ray answered truthfully.

Then I asked The Family how long they were staying here.

"We were waiting for you," Nell answered.

"What did Verla mean in her letter, *until the heat cools?*"

T.P. answered for Verla:

"She wasn't sure how all those men would react after getting canned."

"But Verla took care of that," Nell added. "It was Verla's idea that the men had to think they were fired for submitting and signing-off on phony invoices paid for bogus unaccountable goods delivered."

"Ray's phony gloves, aprons, and knives?"

"Correct," Nell said.

"So, all the men don't know they were fired for Sisters of Mercy?" I asked.

"Right. Even my step-dad, Bob Jasper, doesn't know. Verla only wanted the board of directors to know…to protect The Family."

"That helped close the deal, fast," T.P. injected. "No publicity…*guaranteed.* If those guys were canned for being thieves…life goes on," T.P. chuckled and coughed, spitting blood into his hanky.

When I asked Ray what he was going to do now, Jane answered for him:

"He's going to sell the A-frame and move to South America."

"Columbia," Ray clarified with a smile.

Then, I surprised myself when I asked Ray how much he wanted for the A-frame.

"A hundred grand," he said. Then he said to me, "Billy, I'll sell it to you for eighty…*cash.*"

***

Three days later, I wrote:

"It feels like I may never write a 2nd book in this 'space of awareness' that my mom said she's always had inside her and knew I would realize some day. My dreams and my question, 'who's watching the watcher?' was enough for me. I didn't need a near-death experience to realize there is a God essence inside all of us. It was my unconscious characters in my book that allowed me to have this experience. How strange is that? When I left

The Hill after saying my goodbyes to all my characters, Nell went with me to my bank and helped me set up a trust fund like the one she set up for The Home. I closed my Tightwad Energy account, returned all my unsold product to Max and closed my account with him. The next day, I drove my van to a body shop, leaving it overnight for them to remove my vehicle lettering along with a new paint job, green, the same color I showed them on Crystal's chakra chart. During my walk home from the body shop I was open to finding out if I could live in that A-frame. I walked to the parking lot of The Argo and felt this sensation that coming to Woodbury could be a dream. But who is dreaming it...and watching it? If I had this experience much earlier of my true Self...I know now that I could have never written "Tightwad Energy" because now I know that the world doesn't need another 'story' that only entertains busy minds. My dad could never give up on his writing. Can I?"

The Green Note

Tony was hanging-on until the bicentennial in '76. He said he wanted to leave this world with fireworks going off all over the country. Mrs. Patino moved to New Hampshire to live with their daughter after they sold their house; she didn't want to be around her husband in The Home on his final days. *"She's too weak for that,"* T.P. told Verla on the phone when Verla said that she and Crystal were flying-in July 2nd to Omaha from San Diego. Verla told me she had to see her old friend before he passed; and my mom wanted to see me and my A-frame I'd bought from Ray before he left for Columbia.

I picked up Crystal and Verla at the airport in Tony's car that he gave me when he moved into The Home. First thing Crystal said to me:

"Your ego has dropped out of your eyes."

I didn't tell her or Verla that I could now see that *light* in my mother's eyes that my dad wrote about. And Verla: Wow! She'd lost over 60 pounds and had her natural brunette hair back, and short, "Styled by Verla," she laughed her beautiful/loud way.

The Sapp sisters wanted to drive by *the old Sapp House*, where they spent their early years with their biological parents before they were killed in a car accident. I caught my mind wishing I'd brought my notebook, and let it pass...something I was getting better at and doing quite often.

I parked T.P.'s car on the shoulder of the old highway that ran north and south on the western edge of the Loess Hills. We got out and stood together leaning against the car while gazing up at the old 2-story "cold and drafty place" Verla commented, and my mother agreed with a nod. My mind wanted to ask them what they were thinking now upon returning to this place that helped decide who they'd become in many ways. There was no sadness or even stories about their past lives here.

Then, my mom started to talk about what we could create now with the money we all knew we didn't deserve.

"Verla and I want to donate our apartments in The Home for a *safe house* for kids and their single moms to live when they have no options."

Then Verla said that she called Jane and Ray, and Nell, and they're all willing to donate their four apartments, adding:

"T.P.'s on-board with it. He told me that half the money from his share goes to care for his wife, and he's open to donating his apartments for a good cause like that."

"That's terrific. How'd you come up with this?" I asked Crystal.

"When Verla and Danny came out to visit us, Verla didn't want Danny to know about the big sale. We started talking about how we could do something good with this money that was positive...and we thought of this place," Crystal nodded at the old Sapp House. "We know there are plenty of single moms in need of a safe place to go...after our experiences here."

"We got lucky with decent foster parents. But they couldn't undo the damage done here," Verla said.

Crystal put her arm around her sister and said that *from something bad, we can make something good happen.*

"I want to go see T.P.," Verla said.

***

During our drive to The Home, I told the Sapp sisters that about every day I'd walk down to visit Tony; sometimes twice a day when he wanted me to pick up something from the store for him. Since there was no smoking in The Home, chewing gum was always on his list, along with some kind of candy bar or ice cream treat.

Not long after moving into the A-frame, my mom convinced me that I'd move forward with my new life if I called all my Tightwad Energy customers and let them know I was out of business and decided not to publish my book. Crystal also told me to keep my list of customers, and to leave *open* the possibility of a 2nd book in case I wanted to market it to them. It took me a few months to call them all. Crystal was right. My customers thanked me for calling; and each call gave me a bit of closure after abruptly ending my route and not following through with my book they all wanted to buy. Verla and Crystal really encouraged me to begin another book, "a story that's all yours," Verla said. Only my mom understood when I let them know I don't have a desire to write another book now, and that *the world doesn't need another story.*

I kept asking them about this idea of theirs for a *safe house* for families in need, and how that could really change my attitude about writing if my first book made a positive difference and helped somebody besides *The Family.* When I told my passengers that I'd commit to giving half of my share for a good project like this –the women began talking about The Home, and how that was their motivation for expanding Sisters of Mercy the way they did, explaining how *that* was the only reason they kept the service growing to all those other locations owned by one big buyer. "That was T.P.'s salesmanship that he turned over to Ray," Verla said. Then my mom said that she pitched the idea to my dad first as an idea for a script, "but he dismissed it because he resented Verla and Ray using his short story, "Sister of Mercy," and not cutting him in from the get-go." Then my mom said that my dad was totally negative about it and threatened to sue Verla and Ray for using his story to create their *salacious* service.

***

I parked in front of The Home after picking up a hot fudge sundae for Tony at the Harlan DQ. Crystal was impressed with the finished building and gave herself a tour of the place she'd only seen photos of.

Verla went into T.P.'s apartment alone with his treat. I stood outside Tony's open door watching and listening

235

to their reunion. T.P. was napping on his hospital bed, his oxygen tubes inserted as the new Mrs. Gordon put his ice cream in the freezer section of his little fridge. I could see Tony open his little brown eyes when she stepped up to his bedside and stroked his arm.

"Look at you," he whispered and smiled.

I lost it when I saw Verla drop her head down and onto her best friend's chest, sobbing uncontrollably while saying things to him I could not make out. Then, the old salesman stroked the back of her brunette head tenderly:

"Your natural color," he whispered hoarsely.

"You like it?" she looked up at him.

"Yes…it's the way it looked when I first met you. You remember?"

She nodded in agreement, crying more and more after showing him her wedding ring.

"This is the place we worked for," he said.

More nodding.

"How do you like my apartment?"

"I like it," she cried, holding both of his hands while telling him he was the father she never had.

"That's why you'd never go out with me," he chuckled and coughed.

I had to get away from this plaintive scene while Verla showed T.P. photos of her life with Fireman Dan in Ensenada. I walked with my mom up to the A-frame, taking the backway trail through the woods. She told me that earlier this week she and Verla had set up a meeting with Nell to discuss this *safe house* project for The Home. Nell – the perfect Yellow – said she'd research it and have data ready, as well as setting up a meeting with Jane this week. Nell told me that Jane was lonely and *out-of-sorts* ever since Ray left for Columbia. Nell said that her mother was considering selling her house and moving into The Home, since Jane was having trouble moving and often dizzy from medication, and not inclined to make meals for herself.

Standing together on the A-frame's deck after a tour of the place, Crystal said this was the perfect home for a writer. She asked me if I'd met any girls since moving here.

"Not yet. I'm enjoying my space here."

Then my mom asked me something she'd never asked me before, whether growing up in a house with parents who lived separate lives had hurt my social life.

"I can't say it has. I know that you and Verla are happy now, and you both deserve to be happy. I don't want to settle for somebody just because I live alone. I've been watching my friend Tony get weaker by the day. You know he's the one who really helped me sell my dream product so that I was able to write my book. I don't know if I could've written it as a busboy in Sammy's."

"Verla feels grateful to be here for him. And I know she really felt conflicted about using your book to sell her service. You must know by now that I was the one who sent you to Verla to write your book. It was my idea to have Verla encourage you to write it for the big sale and put your dad's name on it."

Crystal removed a folded piece of green paper from her violet and white vest pocket and handed it to me, saying:

"I gave this to your dad after one of his script rejections. He didn't take it to heart as intended. I thought about giving it to you many times. It might help you decide whether you want to keep writing or not."

I opened the green paper and read it out loud:

"Rid me of the ego and the illusion of separation from my true Self."

I remembered these words:

"This is what you told me to do in high school…to stay open in my heart."

Then I told Crystal about my 2 dreams; she was the one person I knew who could really understand what they meant. After I'd told her about *the watcher*, she agreed with my analogy of my true Self being awakened, adding:

"Most of my clients had to be shocked awake by some trauma because of their conditioned mind's construction of the ego. From my experience, most with intentions of just *wanting* consciousness will not dissolve the ego until suffering becomes unbearable."

"That reminds me…I've been waiting for you and Verla to help me with something tomorrow…"

"On Independence Day," she said.

No More Stories

*"Dad, I know now that my true Self is not my story.
Chapters come and go like clouds across the sky. We
are the sky, Dad. Your life and stories helped me realize
this. You, Mom, Aunt Verla and her family of characters
led me to the greatest gift of all: my true Self. I love
you."*

I crumpled and balled the note with my hand and
tossed it into the rising flames of my dad's writing
crate placed in the middle of an open barbeque pit
behind Paul's little farmhouse located just a few
miles northeast of Denison. Crystal and Verla were with
me; I was happy they were able to keep this scene
drama-free as we stood together facing the burning crate.

Last night, the three of us were on the A-frame deck
after setting up a meeting with Jane and Nell at Jane's
house that we had earlier this morning after breakfast.
We talked about the *big sale* and where it goes from
here. Crystal said, *no more stories, no more means to an
end.* Verla agreed with her sister; and then my aunt
started to talk about her late-night moments on the ledge
of The Argo, something I certainly would've put in my
book if I'd known.

"When I was standing on that cold ledge alone, naked and hungover in total darkness…I wanted to jump…and be out of this world. Then I thought about what Ray saw on his way to the hospital. His experience made me want to stay…and prove to my selfish ego that I could turn my life into something good that makes a real positive difference. That's when I heard the firetrucks coming closer and closer…so I stayed put. And there was Danny…this stranger…this man who could be one of my old customers or a customer of Sisters of Mercy for all I knew… And when he reached out for me I saw his eyes…so calm and steady… And everything about my past left me… It was as if it had fallen away. Ever since then we've been together. And I *know* I wouldn't even have this life if I hadn't been Verla Sapp and my sad story on that ledge."

I watched my mother embrace her big sister, for only Crystal knew Verla's early chapters. We stood there watching the growing flames of the crackling pine box of stories. We were all thrilled about our earlier meeting with Nell and Jane. Jane decided to sell her house and move into The Home, as both Jane and her daughter were *excited* about children in-need living in The Home. That's when Nell suggested we use her boyfriend's barbeque pit to burn my dad's crate, and so we followed Jane out to Paul's farm.

As the orange flames blackened the crate, Nell invited us into the house for coffee and tea, and ginger cookies, to talk more about this *foundation* she could easily set up as a *temporary shelter* for families living in the county. Later that night on the deck I wrote about the long day we had:

240

*"From the farmhouse kitchen window I could see the
orange-glowing blackened remains of my father's crate,
his last pages vain-licking the sweet air of silage and
dung for more fire and ash. Having my mother near me
was enough to remind me to let this dying form go. This
burning of D. D. Wadstone's past life altered something
in me, this subtle reminder to keep some of my attention
inside and separated from the form of the world.*

*Later, Verla and my mom and I walked into the
Denison malt shop, the nostalgic business where
Donna's beautiful face framed the walls. Verla wanted
to get T.P. something cold for his white-hot throat
numbed with powerful drugs. This attractive young
woman with auburn hair named 'Kim' (on her name tag)
served us, scooping a pint of lemon sherbet for T.P. to be
saved for us in a carryout container kept in the freezer
until we finished our treats. We sat at a table looking
out at the clean town of Denison, watching life come and
go, the Sapp sisters licking their ice cream cones while I
sipped down a root beer float from a frozen glass
fountain mug. I could sense these women were up to
some kind of matchmaking when my mother asked me if I
knew that girl who served us. I told them I've seen her
before. Verla laughed after telling me she didn't see a
ring on her finger. I told them that maybe she can't
wear any rings scooping ice cream. When Verla was
getting T.P.'s treat, my mom and I walked up close to
this black and white photo of Donna hanging on the
wall, similar to the same one that was in my father's
crate. I asked my mom again if she recalled my dad
saying anything about Donna or why he kept her picture
in his crate. My mom said he always liked Donna, and
one of the reasons my dad was angry with Verla's*

241

'service' was because Verla once sent me a photo of herself wearing a wig she called 'The Donna Reed.' That was another thing I would've put in my book if I had known. We left the shop and when we returned to The Home, an ambulance was there, removing Tony's covered body on a gurney after passing away 'a couple hours ago,' Roberta told us. Verla had the paramedics stop, so she could see her friend's face for the last time. It was smiling at us, as if reminding Verla of what Ray experienced. 'He let go,' Verla said, handing me the ice cream and telling the men she wanted to ride with her friend to the funeral home and stay with him for a while.

My mom and I watched the fireworks from my deck that night. We were waiting for Verla to call to tell us she was ready for us to come and get her. When I asked Crystal why Verla hadn't called by now, she said, 'I know my sister; she'll call when she's ready.' Around 10 that night, when the big fireworks display ended, Verla called and said to pick her up on the courthouse square in Denison. My mom wanted me to go alone, telling me she wanted to call Val before going to bed."

Mustard and Cupcake

Verla was sitting with her hands folded on her lap, on the same bench on the town square where we'd sat together that day Ray rejected her soon after he'd awakened from his coma. I could tell she'd been crying by the puffiness under her eyes and by the way her shoulders slumped forward as if she'd been squeezing memories of T.P. from her heart. I sat next to her and held her left hand; I could feel the diamond ring Danny gave her in Vegas, loose on her finger from all the weight she'd lost.

We cried together. My tears were for her loss. I knew from dozens of mornings of seeing and hearing Tony and Verla in Sammy's that their friendship was older than me, with ten thousand days and nights of friendship through forty thousand seasons. I asked her to:

"Tell me one of your favorite memories of T.P."

She sniffed and cleared her throat; she appeared to be sifting through her memories...until a soft chuckle turned to a full-blown Verla cackle.

243

"What?"

"One winter day, it was so cold, and T.P.'s heat was out in his apartment... This was when he was single and lived in this dump. He had two hamsters: Mustard and Cupcake. Mustard had this yellow stripe across his white back and Cupcake was all-white. One morning he brought the hamsters in their cage to Sammy's, wanting me to keep them in my place since he was going on the road and didn't want them to freeze in his apartment. So, I put the cage in Sammy's office and put them in Birdie's trunk a few minutes before my shift was over. Al called me before I left Sammy's and said he needed me right away to tend bar, to come in early. So, I went straight to Al's, forgetting all about the hamsters until I was nearly asleep in my bed after my shift. I was so *scared* running downstairs to my car in my bare feet and found them frozen stiff in their cage. Next day I went to a pet store and bought two hamsters resembling the others. When T.P. came over to pick up his hamsters... I had to confess right away. He saw how bad I felt and consoled me. Then, a while later, it was my birthday and he came into Sammy's with a wrapped present for me. I opened the present and there was a jar of mustard and a white cupcake. Then he gave me a birthday card that said, *Happy Birthday! We love you!* It was signed, *Mustard and Cupcake.*"

End of Time

Crystal and Verla stayed with me for nearly 3 weeks, until The Home was converted to a safe haven shelter, alive and vibrant and teeming with 11 children and their mothers residing in four of the apartments. Each family had their temporary rent-free apartment with a daycare that kept Roberta, Nell - and even Jane - busier than ever while the mothers were quickly placed by Nell in full and part-time employment in Mapleton, Denison, and Harlan. 20% of the money earned by the mothers went directly to The Home Foundation to cover some of the costs for 3 healthy meals a day. Crystal gave all the moms chakra readings, all positive messages that gave these women-in-need a sense that they were starting over from a safe place. My mom would spend hours at a time alone with each new single mother and give each one the undivided attention I'd seen her give a thousand times in our Culver City home every Saturday. Most of these single moms had zero support, which Crystal said was far better than the unconscious family and friends who would only keep them unconscious. She taught them to meditate, to hear the habitual negative thoughts they were not even aware of. Each day, whether the resident mother was working or not –had a one-hour session with Crystal that included meditation and body awareness.

My job was transportation, giving rides to and from work for 3 of the 4 mothers, plus any doctor appointments. Verla was doing all of the cooking and clean-up for the 11 children in each of the 4 apartments while hawkish Roberta and sweet Jane kept love and order flowing in The Home. All of us were committed to keeping expenses down and getting the families on their feet asap. Even farmer Paul would deliver bushels of sweetcorn and potatoes from his garden. Another job I had: keeping the floors and windows clean, as well as a trip to the county dump once a week in my van.

Tony had left Verla nearly 400K, a gift Verla didn't know about until T.P.'s attorney contacted her via Sammy a few days before she and my mom were to fly to San Diego, back to Danny and Val. I drove my mom and Verla to Woodbury where we had lunch with Sammy, Tommy, and Al, at Sammy's. While Verla and Crystal stayed to catch-up with Verla's friends, I picked up some paper and janitorial supplies for The Home at Max Hermann's, getting my old jobber prices from Max. We talked about Tony, and how Mrs. Patino was thankful that Verla was there to see that Tony's ashes (as he wished) were scattered outside his apartment window where he spent his last days. Mrs. Patino didn't know about the *big sale* or know where the 500K came from that Tony sent their daughter to care for his wife in New Hampshire. Max told me that Tony stopped in to see him just before he moved to The Home, and that Tony sold his house for 180K and sent all of it to his daughter. That reminded me of what Verla lamented about T.P. on our drive here, that, "T.P. took care of everybody but himself."

Old Max wanted to know about Verla and her new life with her husband in Mexico. I told him how happy they were living next door to my mother in a villa they bought for 40K. I didn't mention Val, since old Max wouldn't understand their relationship. Max stood on the dock while I loaded my supplies into the spacious trunk of Tony's wife's car. That was another surprise for Max, when he heard that his ex-salesman gave me his car when he moved into The Home.

Jane told me that Nort bought The Hill from her and was converting the *hotel* to one-room apartments. After I left Max, I drove over to the corner bookstore, wanting to give Verla more time with her friends. There was a reason I wanted to go into that place again, something I had reconnected with during Crystal's visit that she called, *end of time*. It's about keeping some of my attention in my body instead of the man-made killer clock that makes the mind go from one thought to the next, an unconscious habit I was addicted-to whenever I'd go into Nort's. This would be a good test for me.

I opened and entered the front door, the same *tinkling* bell overhead announcing my arrival. Nort and his wife were standing near the register. I was aware of my attention inside me when both of them smiled at me. I pulled an RC from the pop cooler and the new owners of The Hill actually made small talk:

"Haven't seen you around," Nort said after counting 4 quarters from his register into my open hand.

"I bought a house in the country."

"Oh! No wonder! You moved," he almost smiled.

"I hear you bought The Hill, next door," I pointed behind him.

"Yes, it's so expensive, getting the rooms ready to rent," he raised his hands over his head as his wife gave her agreeing negative nod while I headed for the pinball machine with my cold RC.

As I kept some of my awareness inside me while playing pinball, I was pleased with my test. No negative thoughts. Again, I was aware of this gap of awareness I'd lost years ago in Culver City when I chose to live in my head with my dad. As I kept passing my test moment to moment I could smell a hint of sweet pipe tobacco wafting from the back of the store, proving to me that my senses were sharpened and I was more aware of life around me. This was Crystal's *end of time*.

Heart Awareness...

Crystal and Verla have kept their promise to return to The Home every 6 months over the last few years, to work with families who have continuously occupied 6 of the 8 apartments since it became an accredited safe haven for local families in need of temporary living space. I have earnestly lived Crystal's words about heart awareness and know the real positive changes manifested all around me.

Grandma Jane and Roberta have lived in adjoining apartments since Jane sold her house. Nell married Paul and they adopted twin girls who had lived in The Home with their heroin-addicted mother until the mother vanished one day and never returned, leaving her kids behind.

Organized Nell does great work keeping the resident mothers employed in local businesses until each mom can support her family outside The Home without welfare assistance. This is a remarkable feat considering The Home was never originally intended to help these families in need. There was no tightwad energy here. Thanks to Nell's business savvy combined with Jane and Roberta's care –the flow of love and money was constant. Donations were coming from many benefactors. Nell said that The Family Foundation went from expenditures of 300K annually to 30K after only 3 years. The interest paid from annuities Nell had set up was now covering all the expenses to keep the doors open.

My work here is so fulfilling – compared to peddling garbage bags and fiction – that I've never thought of doing anything else. Every November and December I've tele-marketed for donations that raise money for The Home, a tax shelter instrument that has managed to keep us afloat in the land of tightwad energy. For those 2 months I pound the phone like D. D. Wadstone, another talent I inherited from him. Crystal has kept me in touch with my true Self by experiencing her words: *Heart awareness is who I am.* So true these words can be. And like any words, they are only words to toss in the mind until you experience the subtle increase in peace and aliveness that has always been there. My true Self was never Billy Wadstone's story. I know that now.

A few weeks after Verla and Crystal flew back after their first visit here together, I went back to the old-fashioned malt shop in Denison with my notebook. I had this notion to write this note to the girl who served us, the same girl with the auburn hair who scooped Tony's ice cream for Verla that 4th of July when Tony passed away. She was working. Her name tag: *Kim* – was all I needed.

"Kim, it's easy to write words to someone I really don't know, yet almost impossible to let you read them. The last time I was in here, I introduced myself and we shook hands. Then, I overheard you talking to someone about how you were going to be like Donna Reed, single until

you can get away from this town and move to California. You reminded me that I had lived in the same city where Donna made a name for herself. I left California to live here, to get away from a place that many believed was magical and special and far away from here, the place my father called the land of tightwad energy. I discovered a place near here in the Loess Hills, a hidden gem of rural isolation that no city could ever create in a million years. Now I live in these hills, enjoying my life here as I never could before.

My father was a Hollywood script writer, who wrote mostly teleplays for TV episodes. He always searched for his one good reader. I found mine in these same hills north of here. She was here, in this shop, not long ago when she and my mother were visiting. They asked me if I knew you. When I'm in here, Donna's picture reminds me of a dream I had while asleep on these hills, a dream that fell from my subconscious mind by the grace of God we all have. My mother defined this dream during her stay with me: 'Heart awareness is who I am.' Billy."

Just then: her voice was there while wiping off a nearby table:

"What are you writing?" Kim asked me.

"It's something I might put in a book…if I ever publish it.

***

The next time I stopped into that malt shop, maybe 2 weeks later, Kim had moved to San Diego to live with her sister. That's what the new girl told me when I asked if Kim was working. I sat at the same window

251

table where I could see the town square; then, I'd see Donna's smiling face on the wall. I wondered if Kim would return home, which to me was just starting to mean *the home* we seem to lose along our busy way in the mind of *doing.* Seated there in that malt shop I was already feeling that subtle awareness of home in my heart by keeping more and more attention on my heart with every breath, allowing more space to dismiss more and more useless thoughts that come and go.

***

One bright Sunday in July of '80 I stopped into the same malt shop. It was the day after hearing that Ray Vining died in Columbia. I was in Jane's apartment cleaning her windows when Ray's American banker in Bogata called Jane to inform her of Ray's passing, and that Ray had named her executor in his will, confirming bank account information he needed in order to send Jane nearly 200K. Like Tony, the banker said that Ray's request was to have his ashes scattered without delay. I stayed there with Jane when she called Nell to let her know of her father's passing. Last night I wrote from my deck:

"Today Jane found out that Ray died in Columbia. She didn't seem shocked or grief-stricken, perhaps because her frail body couldn't handle such emotions. After calling Nell, Jane asked me for Verla's phone number. Unlike Nell's calm matter-of-factness, I could hear Verla's distinct telephone voice filled with concerned emotion, as Jane explained that the banker told her that the constable reported in Bogata that there was no foul play, that Mr. Vining died peacefully in bed. I could

hear Verla ask: 'In Ray's bed?' That gave Jane a chuckle.

I walked outside and circled The Home; I could hear and see Roberta reading to the children through the open windows in the central daycare area. I couldn't help from knowing that Ray played a big role in making The Home a reality. Like Tony, Ray never did see this place as a safe haven for the families that live here. If I ever choose to go back to the dead past –I'd see now how that kind of pain and suffering that was part of Sisters of Mercy, made this place possible. Oh, how I wasted time pre-judging Ray as this creepy guy that somehow Verla loved and cared for, as if Ray was some brother in pain that only she could know. How can I drop all judgments and labels from my conditioned mind, now that I know someone like Ray Vining had it in him to make The Home a reality?"

***

Now, I sit here in the same malt shop, looking out at this quiet/busy little town in the fall of 1980, *knowing* there's no place I'd rather be than here right now, living on the same hills where my parents discovered each other, and gave me this chance to experience it while I'm young. How fortunate *I am*.

The End

Thanks to my library directors
and readers who keep me writing.

www.michaelfrederick82.com